GCSE

VISUAL
REVISION
GUIDE

SUCCESS

PHYSICS
FOUNDATION

Author
Brian Arnold

CONTENTS

ELECTRICITY AND ELECTROMAGNETISM

ATOMS AND RADIOACTIVITY

THE EARTH AND BEYOND

SPEED, VELOCITY AND ACCELERATION

SPEED AND VELOCITY

We often use the words <u>speed</u> and <u>velocity</u> as if they have the same meaning, but there is a small yet important difference.
- A speed tells us how fast an object is moving.
- A velocity tells us how fast an object is moving and in which direction.
- 20 m/s is a speed. 20 m/s northwards is a velocity.

HOW TO CALCULATE SPEED AND VELOCITY

The **speed** or **velocity** of an object is a measure of **how fast it is moving**.
To find the speed of an object we need to know how far it has travelled and how long it took to travel this distance. Then we use the equation:

speed = <u>distance</u> or $v = \dfrac{d}{t}$
       time

We can write this equation as a formula triangle. We cover the quantity the question is asking us to calculate. The triangle now shows us the formula we should use.

EXAMPLE
A sprinter runs 400 m in 50 s. Calculate his speed.

$v = \dfrac{d}{t}$

$v = \dfrac{400 \text{ m}}{50 \text{ s}}$

$v = 8$ m/s

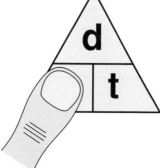

EXAMPLE
A cricket ball travels at 50 m/s for 2 s after being hit. How far has the ball travelled?

Using the formula triangle we see that <u>distance = speed x time</u>, or <u>d = v x t</u>

$d = v \times t$
$d = 50 \times 2$
$d = 100$ m

EXAMPLE
A car travels 200 km at an average speed of 40 km/h. How long does the journey take?

Using the formula triangle we see that

time = <u>distance</u>, or $t = \dfrac{d}{v}$
      speed

$t = \dfrac{d}{v}$
$t = \dfrac{200}{40}$
$t = 5$ hr

Examiner's Top Tip
Practise using your formula triangle. It is very useful for many formulæ you will need in your exams.

ACCELERATION

If an object is <u>changing</u> its speed or its velocity it is <u>accelerating</u>. The acceleration of an object tells us <u>how</u> <u>rapidly</u> <u>its</u> <u>speed</u> <u>is</u> <u>changing</u>.

EXAMPLE

A motorcyclist has an acceleration of 20 km/hr per s. This means his speed increases by 20 km/h each second.

A rocket has an acceleration of 50 m/s per s(sometimes written as 50 m/s^2). This means that the rocket increases its speed by 50 m/s every second.
To calculate the acceleration of an object we need to know by how much its speed or velocity has changed and how long this change in velocity has taken. Then we use the equation:

$$\text{acceleration} = \frac{\text{change in velocity}}{\text{time taken}}$$

where the Δ symbol (the Greek letter 'delta') means 'change in'.

EXAMPLE

A racing car accelerates from rest to a speed of 100 m/s in just 5 s. Calculate the acceleration of the car.

$a = \dfrac{\Delta v}{t}$

$a = \dfrac{100}{5}$

$a = 20$ m/s^2

The bobsleigh team is about to increase its speed from 0 m/s to 50 m/s in 10 s. Calculate its acceleration.

$a = \dfrac{\Delta v}{t}$

$a = \dfrac{50}{10}$

$a = 5$ m/s^2

QUICK TEST

1. What two measurements do you need to calculate the speed of an object?

2. Name two units you could use to measure the speed of an object.

3. Calculate the speed of a man who runs 70 m in 14 s.

4. How long will it take a man running at 10 m/s to travel 550 m?

5. How far will a car travel in 3 h if its speed is 60 km/h?

6. Calculate the acceleration of an object which increases its speed by 60 m/s in 20 s.

6. 3 m/s^2.
5. 180 km.
4. 55 s.
3. 5 m/s.
2. m/s, km/h.
1. Distance travelled and time taken.

GRAPHS OF MOTION I

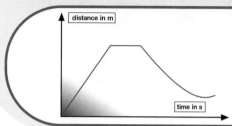

It is often useful to show the <u>journey</u> <u>of an object</u> in the form of a <u>graph</u>. There are two types of graph: the first of these is the <u>distance–time graph</u>.

DISTANCE–TIME GRAPHS

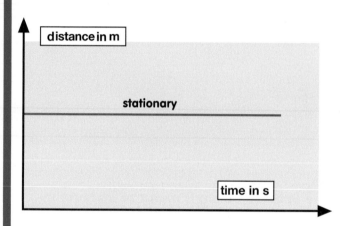

Horizontal line: object is <u>not</u> <u>moving</u>.

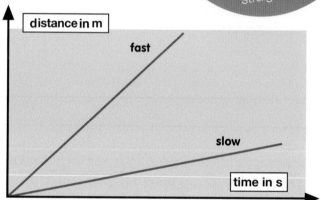

Sloping straight line: object moving at <u>constant</u> <u>speed</u>. Steeper straight line: object moving at a <u>greater constant speed</u>.

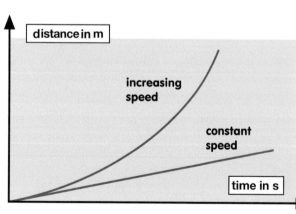

Steepness or gradient of line changes: speed of object is <u>not</u> <u>constant</u>.

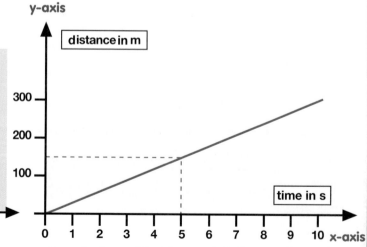

<u>Speed</u> of an object is equal to the <u>gradient of the line</u>.

Speed of object $= \dfrac{y}{x} = \dfrac{150}{5} = 30$ m/s

EXAMPLE

A bus moving at a constant speed travels 2000 m in 100 s. It then stops for 50 s to pick up passengers. Continuing its journey, the bus, again moving at a constant speed, travels 1000 m in the next 100 s.

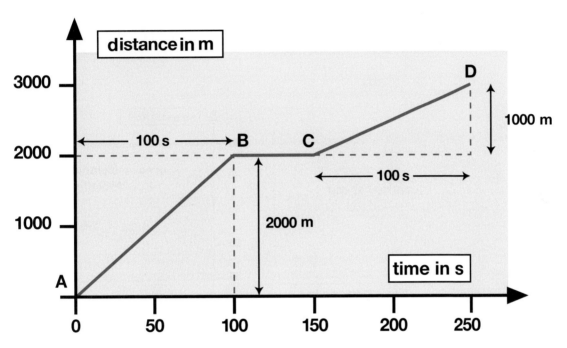

QUICK TEST

1. On a distance–time graph what do the following show?

   a) a horizontal line

   b) a steeply sloping straight line

   c) a straight line sloping just a little.

2. Draw a distance–time graph to show the following journey:

   A motorcyclist moving at a constant speed travels 400 m in 10 s. He then stops for the next 10 s before travelling 600 m at a constant speed in the next 10 s.

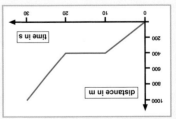

1. a) a stationary object
   b) greater constant speed
   c) lesser constant speed.
2. See graph

GRAPHS OF MOTION II

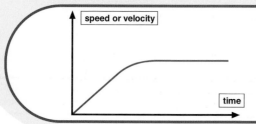

The second type of graph we can use to show the <u>journey</u> <u>of</u> <u>an</u> <u>object</u> is the <u>speed–</u> or <u>velocity–time</u> <u>graph</u>.

SPEED– OR VELOCITY–TIME GRAPHS

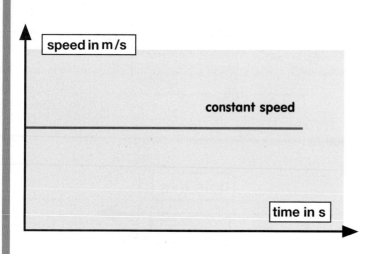

Horizontal line: object moving at <u>constant</u> <u>speed</u>.

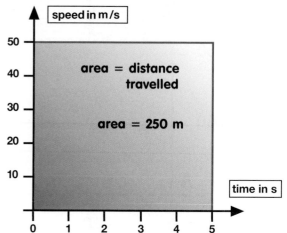

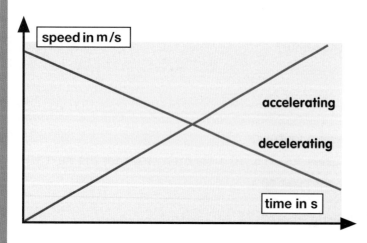

Line sloping upwards: object increasing speed, i.e. <u>accelerating</u>.
Line sloping downwards: object decreasing speed, i.e. <u>decelerating</u>.

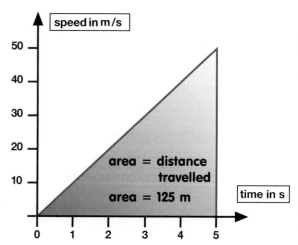

The <u>area</u> under a <u>speed–</u> or <u>velocity–time</u> <u>graph</u> shows the <u>distance</u> an object has travelled.

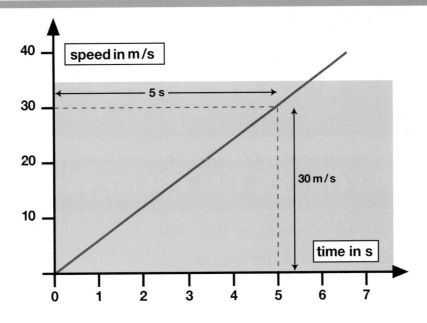

We can find the <u>acceleration</u> of an object by measuring the <u>gradient</u> of its velocity–time (or speed–time graph).

The acceleration of the object in the graph above is:

$$\frac{30 m/s}{5s} = 6 \ m/s^2$$

EXAMPLE
A motorcyclist starting from rest accelerates to a speed of 40 m/s in 4 s. He travels at this speed for 10 s before decelerating to a halt in 8 s.

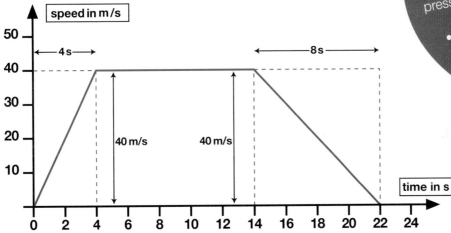

Examiner's Top Tip
If you have to draw a graph remember to:
- use a sharp pencil and don't press too hard. You may want to rub it out!
- use a ruler for straight lines and axes.
- label the axes and include units.

- -

QUICK TEST

1. On a velocity–time graph what do the following show?
   a) a horizontal line
   b) a straight line sloping steeply upwards
   c) a straight line sloping gently downwards.

2. Draw a velocity–time graph to describe the following journey:

   A sprinter starting from rest accelerates to a speed of 10 m/s in 2 s.

   He travels at this speed for the next 8 s then decelerates to 2 m/s in 4 s.

   He continues to jog at this speed for the next 6 s.

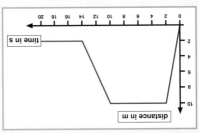

1. a) constant speed
b) large constant acceleration
c) small constant deceleration.
2. See graph

FORCES

EFFECTS OF FORCES ON OBJECTS

When forces are applied to an object they may:

- start the object moving if it is stationary
- stop the object if it is already moving
- speed the object up
- slow the object down
- change the direction of the object.
- change the shape of the object.

MEASURING FORCES

We can measure the size of a force using a **newtonmeter**. This consists of a spring and a scale; the scale measures how much the spring stretches when a force is applied to it. The larger the force the more the spring extends. We measure forces in **newtons** (N). An average-sized apple weighs of about 1 N.

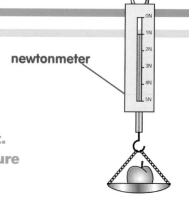

newtonmeter

BALANCED FORCES

If several forces are applied to an object, they may cancel each other out. The forces are balanced.
- If the forces applied to an object are balanced they will have no effect on its motion.
- If the object is stationary it will remain stationary.
- If the object is moving it will continue to move in the same direction and at the same speed.

EXAMPLE

If the driving force of this aircraft equals the drag, it will travel at a constant speed. If the lift force equals the weight, the aircraft will stay at a constant height.

balanced forces: no motion

reaction from table

stationary object

weight

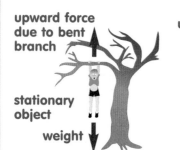

upward force due to bent branch

stationary object

weight

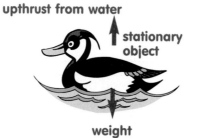

upthrust from water

stationary object

weight

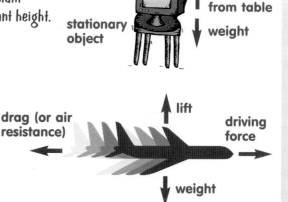

drag (or air resistance)

lift

driving force

weight

UNBALANCED FORCES

- If the forces applied to an object do not cancel each other out, i.e. they are **unbalanced**, they will affect its motion.

- If the object is stationary it may start to move.
- If it is already moving it may:
stop moving
speed up
slow down
change direction.

stationary object
made to move:
unbalanced forces

unbalanced
forces

FORCES AND ACCELERATION

An object whose motion (speed or velocity or direction) is changing is <u>accelerating</u>. The size of the acceleration depends on:

- The size of the force: the larger the force the greater the acceleration for the <u>same</u> mass.
- The mass of the object:.the larger the mass the smaller the acceleration for the <u>same</u> force.

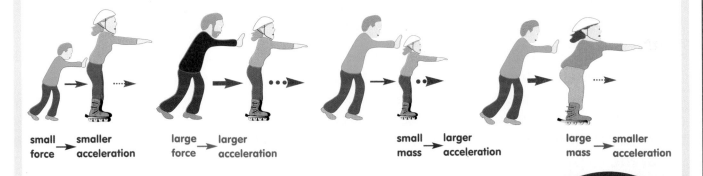

small force → smaller acceleration   large force → larger acceleration   small mass → larger acceleration   large mass → smaller acceleration

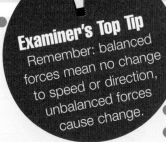

Examiner's Top Tip
Remember: balanced forces mean no change to speed or direction, unbalanced forces cause change.

QUICK TEST

1. Name five things that might happen to an object's motion when a force is applied to it.
2. What do we use a newtonmeter for?
3. In what units do we measure forces?
4. What effect do balanced forces have on the motion of an object?
5. What does the size of the acceleration of an object depend on?

5. Mass of object and size of force.
4. No effect.
3. Newtons (N).
2. To measure the size of a force.
1. Speed up, slow down, stop, start and change direction.

FRICTION AND TERMINAL VELOCITY

FRICTION

Whenever an object moves or tries to move, <u>friction</u> is present.

All moving objects cause friction to occur.

Friction

Friction between surfaces can make them hot and wear them away.

worn brake block

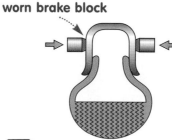

high temperature

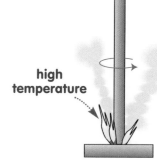

Friction between the tyres of a car and the surface of a road is very important. If there is insufficient grip it is impossible to stop or steer the car safely.

REDUCING FRICTION BY STREAMLINING AND LUBRICATING

- As a bobsleigh travels down the run it gains speed.
- There are large frictional forces at work between the sleigh and the air, and between the runners and the ice.
- To keep these forces to a minimum the bobsleigh is:
  a) streamlined. It is shaped so it cuts through the air with less resistance.
  b) the runners are coated with a lubricant, such as wax.

MOVING THROUGH AIR

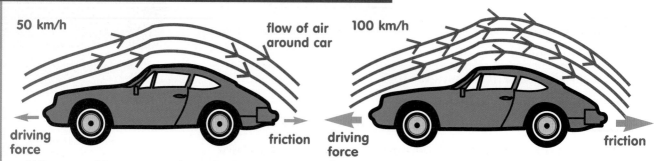

50 km/h

flow of air around car

100 km/h

driving force

friction

driving force

friction

- *When an object moves through air or water it will experience frictional or resistive forces (drag) which will try to prevent its motion.*
- *The faster the object moves the larger these resistive forces become.*

TERMINAL VELOCITY: CARS

Action

The driver begins the journey by pressing the accelerator.

The accelerator is kept in the same position.

The accelerator is kept in the same position.

Result

The driving force from the engine makes the car accelerate.

driving force

As the speed of the car increases the air resistance increases. The car will have a smaller acceleration.

driving force   air resistance

The air resistance and the driving force are equal and balanced. The car travels at a constant speed, known as its terminal velocity.

driving force   air resistance

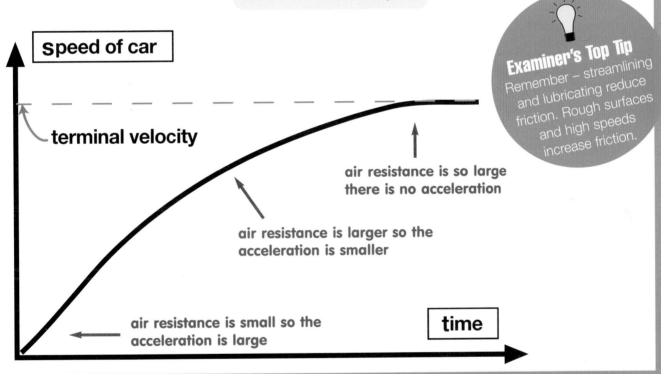

speed of car

terminal velocity

air resistance is so large there is no acceleration

air resistance is larger so the acceleration is smaller

air resistance is small so the acceleration is large

time

Examiner's Top Tip
Remember – streamlining and lubricating reduce friction. Rough surfaces and high speeds increase friction.

QUICK TEST

1. What is friction?
2. In which direction does friction act?
3. What is streamlining?
4. What happens to a moving object if the driving force and the resistive forces are balanced?
5. Name two possible effects of friction between two surfaces.

Examiner's Top Tip
Make sure you can give examples of situations where the presence of friction is an advantage or disadvantage.

1. A force that opposes motion.
2. The opposite direction to motion.
3. Shaping to reduce resistance.
4. It has a constant velocity, or zero acceleration.
5. Heat and wearing away of the surface.

STOPPING A VEHICLE

In order to slow or stop a vehicle a <u>braking force</u> needs to be applied to it. This is usually achieved by using the friction between surfaces.

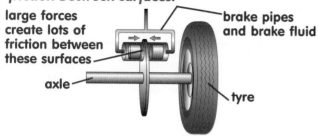

large forces create lots of friction between these surfaces

brake pipes and brake fluid

axle

tyre

- *To avoid accidents it is important that drivers can estimate how much distance they need to bring a vehicle to a halt. This is called the <u>stopping distance</u>.*
- *The stopping distance consists of two parts:*
1. *The thinking distance: this is the distance a vehicle travels before a driver applies the brakes.*
2. *The braking distance: this is the distance the vehicle travels whilst braking.*

THINKING DISTANCE

Things that will affect the thinking distance are:
- *<u>The speed of a vehicle</u>: the greater the speed the greater the distance travelled before the brakes are applied.*
- *<u>The reaction time of the driver</u>: the slower a driver's reactions the greater the distance travelled before the brakes are applied. Drinking alcohol, taking drugs and tiredness will increase this time.*
- *<u>Poor visibility</u>: may delay the point at which a hazard is seen and the brakes applied.*

BRAKING DISTANCE

Things that will affect the braking distance are:

- *<u>The mass of the vehicle</u>: the greater the mass the greater the distance needed to come to a halt.*

- *<u>The speed of the vehicle</u>: this affects the braking distance far more than most people realise. For example, if a driver doubles his speed he will need at least four times more braking distance.*

- *<u>The braking forces applied to the wheels</u>: faulty brakes can result in smaller forces being applied to the wheels, thus increasing the braking distance. But drivers need to be aware that if too great a braking force is applied, friction between the vehicle's tyres and the road surface may not be great enough to prevent skidding.*

- *<u>The frictional forces between the tyres and the road surface</u>: if these are reduced in any way the braking distance will increase. Frictional forces will be lessened in adverse weather conditions e.g. wet or icy; if tyres are worn and so provide poor grip; or if the road surface is smooth.*

STOPPING DISTANCE

Shortest stopping distances, on a dry road, with good brakes:

<u>At 13 m/s (30 m.p.h.)</u>

Thinking distance	Braking distance	Total stopping distance
9 m	14 m	23 m

9 m 14 m
23 m

Thinking Distance

Stopping Distance

<u>At 22 m/s (50 m.p.h.)</u>

Thinking distance	Braking distance	Total stopping distance
15 m	38 m	53 m

15 m 38 m
53 m

<u>At 30 m/s (70 m.p.h.)</u>

Thinking distance	Braking distance	Total stopping distance
21 m	75 m	96 m

21 m 75 m
96 m

STOPPING AND STRETCHING

STRETCHING

WEIGHT, MASS AND GRAVITY

- Mass is the <u>amount</u> <u>of</u> <u>matter</u> there is in an object.
- We measure mass in kilograms (kg).
- Gravity is a force that pulls an object downwards.
- The size of this force is an object's weight. We can calculate the weight of an object using the following equation:

weight = m × g

m is the mass of the object
g is the strength of gravity

- On Earth, g = 10 N/kg (i.e. an object with a mass of 1 kg weighs 10 N on the Earth).
- On the Moon, g = 1.6 N/kg (i.e. an object with a mass of 1 kg weighs 1.6 N on the Moon).

This block has a mass of 6 kg.
It contains 6 kg worth of matter.

On Earth its mass is 6 kg
and its weight is:
weight = m × g = 6 × 10 = 60 N

On the Moon the amount of matter in the block, i.e. its mass, does not change. It is still 6 kg. But its weight is less:
weight = m × g = 6 × 1.6 = 9.6 N

STRETCHING SPRINGS & WIRES

- If we apply a force to a spring or wire it will <u>extend</u>.
- The graph below shows how the extension varies with the applied force.
- The extension is the <u>increase</u> in <u>length</u> of the spring/wire when a force is applied to it.

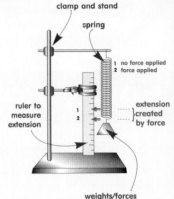

clamp and stand
spring
1 no force applied
2 force applied
ruler to measure extension
extension created by force
weights/forces to stretch the spring

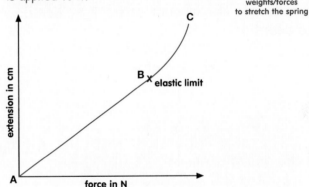

extension in cm

C

B × elastic limit

A

force in N

A–B: a) Because this line is straight, it tells us that the extension of the spring is proportional to the force, i.e. if the force is doubled the extension is doubled.
   b) If the applied force is removed, the spring or wire goes back to its original length
   c) This is called <u>elastic</u> <u>behaviour</u>.

B: This is known as the elastic limit. Beyond this point the behaviour of the spring or wire is no longer elastic.

B–C: a) Because the line is not straight the extension is no longer proportional to the force.
   b) The spring or wire will not return to its original length when the applied force is removed; it has been permanently deformed.
   c) Its behaviour is <u>inelastic</u>.

QUICK TEST

1. Which two distances are added together to find the total stopping distance of a car?
2. Name two things that may affect the thinking distance of a driver.
3. Name three things that may affect the braking distance of a car.
4. A spring extends 3 cm when a weight of 20 N is hung from one end. How much will the spring extend if a force of:
   a) 40 N is hung from it?
   b) 50 N is hung from it?
   c) What assumption have you made?

4. a) 6 cm, b) 7.5 cm, c) Extension is below elastic limit.
3. Mass of vehicle, speed, weather conditions.
2. Speed of vehicle, reaction time.
1. Thinking and braking distances.

WORK AND POWER

What is work? (Do you really want to know?) What is power?
<u>Work</u> is done when a force is applied to an object and the object moves.
<u>Power</u> is the rate at which work is being done.

Examiner's Top Tip
Remember that by using the formula triangle you should be able to calculate the work done or the time taken using the power equation.

DOING WORK

- <u>Work</u> is done when an <u>applied</u> <u>force</u> <u>moves</u> <u>an</u> <u>object</u>.
- This weightlifter is doing work: he is pushing these weights above his head.

To calculate the amount of work he has done we use the equation:

work done = force x distance moved in direction of the force

$$W = F \times d$$

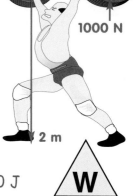

1000 N

2 m

In the above example:
W = 1000 x 2.0 = 2000 J or 2 kJ

- We measure work in <u>joules</u> (J) or <u>kilojoules</u> (kJ). 1 kJ = 1000 J

- It is useful to write the equation as a formula triangle:

EXAMPLE
600 J of work are done when this lawn-mower is pushed 10 m.
Calculate the size of the force pushing the mower.

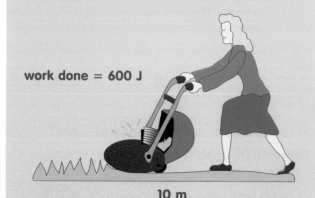

work done = 600 J

10 m

$$F = \frac{W}{d} = \frac{600}{10} = 60 \text{ N}$$

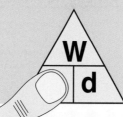

EXAMPLE
Whilst pushing this car with a force of 150 N, 60 kJ (i.e. 60 000 J) of work was done. How far was the car pushed?

pushing force 150 N
work done = 60 kJ

$$d = \frac{W}{F} = \frac{60\,000}{150} = 400 \text{ m}$$

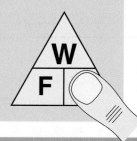

POWER

Power is the rate of doing work, i.e. how much work is done per second.
• *We can calculate the power of a machine using the equation:*

power = $\dfrac{\text{work done}}{\text{time taken}}$ or $P = \dfrac{W}{t}$

$$\dfrac{W}{P \mid t}$$

• We measure power in watts (W) or kilowatts (kW).

EXAMPLE
The power of this car engine is 1000 W. It can do 1000 J of work in one second.

The power of this car engine is 3000 W. It is more powerful. Its engine can do 3000 J of work every second.

CALCULATING POWER

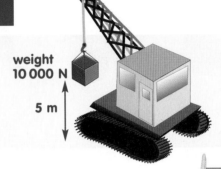

weight 10 000 N

5 m

EXAMPLE
This crane is lifting a 10 000 N load to a height of 5 m.
W = F x d = 10 000 x 5 = 50 000 J or 50 kJ
If the crane can do this in 100 s, its power is:

P = $\dfrac{W}{t}$ = $\dfrac{50\,000}{100}$ = 500 J/s or 500 W

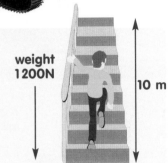

weight 1200N

10 m

EXAMPLE
This man runs 10 m up a flight of stairs in just 5 s. He weighs 1200 N. Calculate the work he does and his power.

W = F x d = 1200 x 10 = 12 000 J or 12 kJ

Remember that the man is doing work due to his vertical motion so it is the vertical distance he moves which is important.

P = $\dfrac{W}{t}$ = $\dfrac{12\,000}{5}$ = 2400 W or 2.4 kW

QUICK TEST

1. Calculate the work done when a lawnmower is pushed 30 m by a force of 250 N.

2. Calculate the height to which a 500 N load is lifted by a crane if 20 kJ of work is done.

3. Calculate the force that is applied to a car engine if 1500 J of work is done when it is lifted on to a bench of height 1 m.

4. What is power?

5. Which units do we use to measure:

   a) work done?

   b) power?

6. Calculate the power of the person pushing the lawnmower in question one if the work is done in 25 s.

7. Calculate the power of the crane in question two if the lift takes 40 s.

7. 500 W.
6. 300 W.
5. a) joules, b) watts.
4. The rate of doing work.
3. 1500 N.
2. 40 m.
1. 7500 J.

MOMENTS

- Forces sometimes make objects <u>turn</u> <u>or</u> <u>rotate</u>.
- The <u>turning</u> <u>effect</u> <u>of</u> <u>a</u> <u>force</u> is called a <u>moment</u>.
- You created a moment with your fingers when you opened this book.

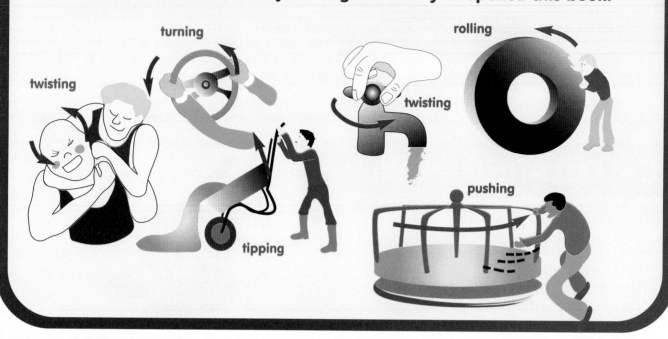

THE SIZE OF A MOMENT

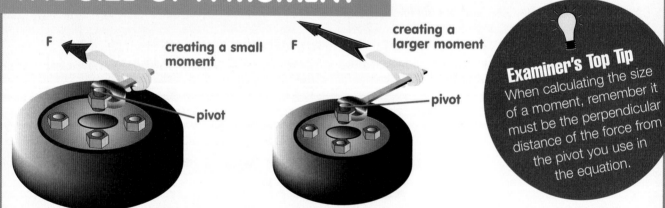

Examiner's Top Tip
When calculating the size of a moment, remember it must be the perpendicular distance of the force from the pivot you use in the equation.

- This moment is trying to undo a nut. The point the spanner will turn around is called the <u>pivot</u>.
- If the nut is too stiff we can increase the size of the moment by:
a) using a longer spanner.
b) applying a bigger force to the spanner.

- The size of a moment can be calculated using the equation:

moment of a force = force x perpendicular distance of force from pivot

We measure moments in Nm.

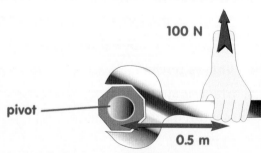

- The moment being applied to this spanner is
100 N x 0.5 m = 50 Nm

BALANCING MOMENTS

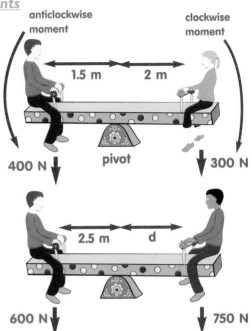

- **If** <u>two</u> <u>equal</u> <u>and</u> <u>opposite</u> <u>moments</u> are applied to an object there will be <u>no turning</u>: the moments are balanced.
- In the opposite diagram, the anticlockwise moments created by the man are balanced by the clockwise moments created by the woman.
- When balanced:

<u>sum</u> <u>of</u> <u>clockwise</u> <u>moments</u> = <u>sum</u> <u>of</u> <u>anticlockwise</u> <u>moments</u>

(known as the Principle of Moments)

anticlockwise moment · · · clockwise moment

1.5 m · 2 m

pivot

400 N · 300 N

If this see-saw balances, the clockwise moment created by the girl must be equal to the anticlockwise moment created by the boy.

300 N x 2.0 m = 400 N x 1.5 m

EXAMPLE

A boy weighing 600 N sits 2.5 m from the centre of a see-saw. His friend weighs 750 N. How far from the centre of the see-saw should his friend sit so that the see-saw balances?

2.5 m · d

600 N · 750 N

- **If the see-saw balances:**

<u>clockwise</u> <u>moment</u> = <u>anticlockwise</u> <u>moment</u>

$$750 \text{ N} \times d = 600 \text{ N} \times 2.5 \text{ m}$$
$$d = \frac{600 \text{ N} \times 2.5 \text{ m}}{750 \text{ N}}$$
$$d = 2.0 \text{ m}$$

Key Terms

Make sure you understand these terms before moving on:
- moment
- pivot
- perpendicular distance
- clockwise and anticlockwise moments

QUICK TEST

1. What is a moment?
2. A force of 200 N is applied perpendicular to and at the end of a spanner 0.4 m long. Calculate the moment created by the force.
3. Suggest two ways in which you could increase the moment applied by the spanner.
4. Under what conditions will two moments applied to the same object balance?
5. A man weighing 1200 N sits 1.5 m to the left of the centre of a see-saw. His friend weighs 1100 N and sits on the opposite side, 1.8 m from the centre. Why does the see-saw not balance?
6. Which way does the seesaw in question five turn?

6. Clockwise.
5. Clockwise moment does not equal anticlockwise moment.
4. Clockwise moment equals anticlockwise moment.
3. Apply a larger force or apply the same force at a point further from the pivot.
2. 80 Nm.
1. The turning effect of a force, defined as force x perpendicular distance of force from pivot.

PRESSURE

Working under pressure is never easy. But if you understand how pressure is created you will deal with it much better.

WHAT IS PRESSURE?

Pressure is a measure of how <u>concentrated</u> or <u>spread</u> <u>out</u> a force is.

• If a force is applied over a <u>small area</u> it creates a <u>large pressure</u>.

• If the same force is applied over a <u>large area</u> it creates a <u>small pressure</u>.

force over small area

force over large area

If a knife is sharp the pressure under its blade is high and cutting the cheese is easy. If the blade is blunt the pressure is lower and cutting the cheese is much more difficult.

If the handles of a carrier bag are thin they can create an uncomfortably high pressure on your hands.

Camels have large feet to prevent them from sinking into the sand.

If all your weight is concentrated on a small area, the pressure created can be very painful.

CALCULATING PRESSURE

We can calculate the pressure created by a force using the equation:

pressure = $\dfrac{force}{area}$ or $P = \dfrac{F}{A}$

• We measure pressure in <u>pascals</u> <u>(Pa)</u>: $1\ Pa = 1\ N/m^2$

EXAMPLE
A crate weighing 1000 N is standing upright on one of its sides which measures 2 m x 2 m. Calculate the pressure created on the ground by the crate.

$P = \dfrac{F}{A} = \dfrac{1000}{4}\ N/m^2 = 250\ Pa$

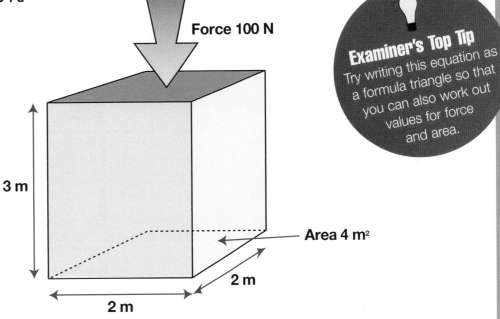

Force 1 N

Area 1 m²

pressure = 1 Pa

Force 100 N

3 m

2 m

2 m

Area 4 m²

Examiner's Top Tip
Try writing this equation as a formula triangle so that you can also work out values for force and area.

- - -

QUICK TEST

1. How do we create a high pressure?

2. How can we avoid or reduce a high pressure?

3. Why are full carrier bags sometimes painful to carry?

4. In what units do we measure pressure?

5. Why does a sharp knife cut through a piece of cheese easier than a blunt knife?

6. Calculate the pressure created when a force of 50 N is over an area of 2.5 m².

7. Calculate the pressure created when a crate weighing 4000 N is standing on the side of the crate which measures 4 m x 2 m.

8. Draw a formula triangle for the equation $P = \dfrac{F}{A}$.

9. What force will create a pressure of 40 Pa when applied to an area of 2 m²?

9. 80 N.

8.

7. 500 Pa.
6. 20 Pa.
5. There is greater pressure under the blade.
4. Pascal (Pa).
3. The weight of the contents is concentrated over a very small area.
2. Spread the force over a large area.
1. By exerting a large force over a small area.

PRESSURE IN A LIQUID

This diver is feeling pressure from the water that is around him.

· The pressure in a liquid <u>increases</u> <u>with</u> <u>depth</u>.

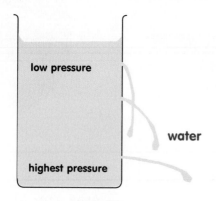

low pressure

water

highest pressure

The water gushes out faster from the lowest hole because pressure in a liquid increases with depth.

The dam wall is thicker at the bottom because this is where the pressure in the water is greatest.

· The pressure in a liquid is the <u>same</u> <u>in</u> <u>all</u> <u>directions</u>.

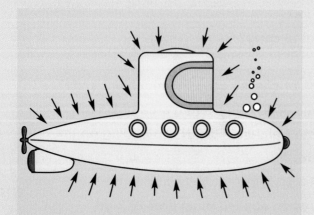

This submarine will feel the same pressure all over its surface.

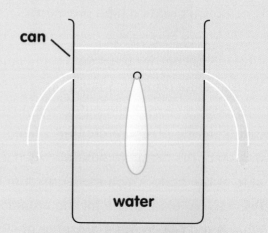

can

water

The water gushes out of all the holes in this can at the same rate; the direction of the hole is unimportant.

HYDRAULIC MACHINES

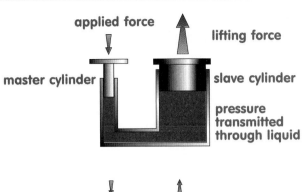

applied force

lifting force

master cylinder

slave cylinder

pressure transmitted through liquid

- Liquids are <u>incompressible</u>. They cannot be squashed.

- As a result, the <u>pressure</u> created by a force is <u>transmitted throughout the liquid</u>. This can be very useful, as the example on the right shows. This arrangement is called a <u>hydraulic jack</u>.

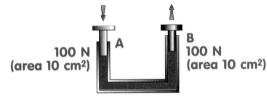

100 N (area 10 cm²)   A   B   100 N (area 10 cm²)

- The jack is a <u>force</u> <u>multiplier</u>: it can be used to lift a heavy object with a small force.

If the slave cylinder has the same area as the master cylinder the forces A and B are the same size.

If the area of the slave cylinder is ten times bigger, the force at D is ten times bigger.

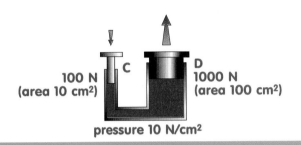

100 N (area 10 cm²)   C   D   1000 N (area 100 cm²)

pressure 10 N/cm²

CAR BRAKES

small force   larger force

Another advantage of using liquids to transmit pressures is that the resulting forces can be applied exactly where they are needed.

- When the driver presses the brake pedal a force is applied to all four wheels <u>at the same time</u>.
- If the slave cylinders are identical the <u>same force</u> will be <u>applied to each wheel</u>.
- Because the master cylinder has a <u>small surface area</u> compared with the slave cylinder, a small force applied to the pedal creates a <u>large braking force</u> on each wheel.

QUICK TEST

1. The pressure in a liquid is the ...... in all directions?
2. Liquids cannot be squashed because they are ...... ? (fill in the missing word)
3. Why is a dam wall thicker at the bottom than the top?
4. Why is a hydraulic jack called a force multiplier?
5. Why would a hydraulic jack not work properly if there were gas bubbles in the liquid?

5. The gas bubbles would become compressed instead of the pressure being transmitted through the liquid.
4. Because the lifting force is greater than the applied force.
3. The water pressure is greater at the bottom.
2. Incompressible.
1. Same

EXAM QUESTIONS – Use the questions to test your progress. Check your answers on page 94.

1. Calculate the speed of a runner who travels 200 m in 20 s.

....

2. Calculate the distance travelled by a motorist who travels at a speed of 90 km/h for three hours.

....

3. Calculate the time it would take for a cyclist travelling at 20 m/s to travel a distance of 500 m.

....

4. State how a driver's tiredness affects the total stopping distance of a vehicle.

....

5. Explain why submarines have to be constructed to withstand large pressures.

....

6. A girl pushes a trolley with a force of 10 N. How much work has she done when the trolley has moved 5 m in the direction of the force?

....

7. Name three things that may happen to an object that is moving with a constant velocity when unbalanced forces are applied to it.

....

8. Explain how the shape of a fish helps it to swim easily through water.

....

9. Look carefully at the graph.
   Explain what is happening to the cyclist between:
   a) A and B..
   b) B and C..
   c) C and D..

10. Name two machines that use liquids to transmit pressure.

....

11. Give two examples of materials that could be used as lubricants.

....

12. Explain why several seconds after jumping from an aircraft a sky diver will be travelling at a constant speed.

....

13. Calculate the moment being created when this door opens.

....

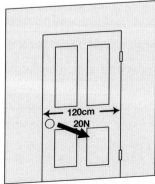

14. Calculate the force that must be applied over an area of 5 m² in order to create a pressure of 4 Pa.

....

15. Calculate the area over which a force of 12 N must act in order to create a pressure of 24 Pa.

....

16. Calculate the acceleration of a car which starting from rest reaches a speed of 30 m/s after 6 s.

....

17. The diagram below shows a stationary object on a flat surface.

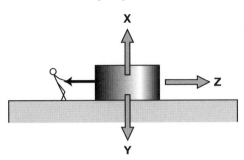

a) Name the forces X, Y and Z..
b) If the object is not moving what can you say about the forces acting on the object?...................
c) If the box has a mass of 3 kg and g = 10 N/kg what is the value of the force Y?......................
d) Suggest two ways in which the friction acting on the object could be reduced.......................

18. A man with a mass of 80 kg runs up 200 steps in 25 s. If the height of each step is 25 cm calculate:
a) the total height climbed by the man..
b) the weight of the man...
c) the work done by the man...
d) the power of the man...
g = 10 N/kg

19. The graph below shows the extension of a wire when forces are applied to it.

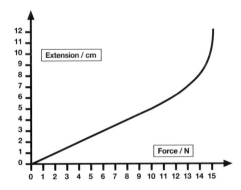

a) What force must be applied to the wire to produce an extension of 5 cm?...............................
b) By how much does the wire extend when a force of 7 N is applied to it?................................
c) What kind of behaviour does the wire show when forces of less than 10 N are applied to it?..............
d) What will happen to the wire if a force of 15 N is applied to it and then removed?......................

ENERGY

- We all need <u>energy</u> in order <u>to be able to do things</u>.
- As human beings we get this energy from the food we eat.
  <u>Food</u> is a form of <u>chemical energy</u>.
- There are several other forms of energy.

DIFFERENT FORMS OF ENERGY

Types of energy	Sources
Heat or thermal energy	Hot objects, e.g. fires
Light energy	The Sun, light bulbs, fires, etc.
Sound energy	Vibrating objects, e.g. loudspeakers
Electrical energy	Available every time a current flows
Chemical energy	Food, fuels and batteries
Kinetic energy (the energy an object has because it is moving)	Flowing water, wind, etc.
Elastic potential energy	Objects such as springs and rubber bands that are stretched or twisted or bent
Gravitational potential energy	Objects that have a high position and are able to fall
Nuclear energy	Reactions that take place in the centre or nucleus of an atom

STORED ENERGY

chemical energy in the wax

elastic potential energy in the rubber band

gravitational potential energy in the water

chemical energy in the battery

- Chemical energy, elastic potential energy and gravitational potential energy are often referred to as forms of <u>stored</u> energy.
- They are forms of energy that are <u>waiting to be used</u>.

EFFICIENCY

The <u>Law of Conservation of Energy</u> states that all the energy that goes into a device must come out. <u>No energy is lost</u>.

In the example opposite, the bulb is not 100% efficient. Not all of the energy is changed into light; some of it is changed into heat.
To calculate the efficiency of a transfer we use the equation:

Efficiency = useful energy output x 100%
total energy input

In this case 200 J of electrical energy enter the bulb, 8 J are changed into light energy and 192 J are changed into heat.

Efficiency = useful energy output x 100%
total energy input

The efficiency of the bulb = $\frac{8}{200}$ x 100% = 4%.

EXAMPLE

200 J of electrical energy

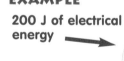

8 J of light energy

192 J of heat energy

ENERGY TRANSFERS

When energy is used <u>it</u> <u>does</u> <u>not</u> <u>disappear</u>. It is <u>transferred</u> <u>into</u> <u>different</u> <u>forms</u> of energy.

A <u>light</u> <u>bulb</u> changes <u>electrical</u> <u>energy</u> into <u>heat</u> <u>and</u> <u>light</u> <u>energy</u>.

A <u>log</u> <u>fire</u> changes <u>chemical</u> <u>energy</u> into <u>heat</u> <u>and</u> <u>light</u> <u>energy</u>.

A <u>loudspeaker</u> changes <u>electrical</u> <u>energy</u> into <u>sound</u>.

electrical energy → light energy
heat energy

chemical energy in logs → heat energy
light energy

electrical energy → sound energy

Other examples of energy changes:

Energy in	Energy changer	Energy out
Chemical (food)	Animal	Heat, kinetic, chemical
Light	Solar cell	Electrical
Kinetic	Wind turbine	Electrical
Strain potential energy	Bow and arrow	Kinetic
Chemical	Battery	Electrical
Electrical	Battery charger	Chemical
Sound	Microphone	Electrical
Electrical	Electric motor	Kinetic
Kinetic	Generator	Electrical
Gravitational potential energy	Falling object	Kinetic
Strain potential energy	Clockwork car	Kinetic

QUICK TEST

1. Name five different types of energy.
2. Name three types of stored energy.
3. What kind of energy does a crate gain as it is lifted by a crane?
4. What kind of energy does water gain as it travels down a waterfall?
5. Write down the energy transfer that takes place when you use a hair drier.
6. How much energy is lost during an energy transfer?
7. Calculate the efficiency of a radio that changes 200 J of electrical energy into 18 J of sound energy.

Examiner's Top Tip
This is another topic that crops up nearly every year in all the exams. Make sure you know lots of examples of energy changes. Write down the names of some machines and devices, then try to describe the energy transfers that take place when they are used.

1. Heat, light, sound, electrical, chemical.
2. Chemical, elastic and gravitational potential energy.
3. Gravitational potential energy.
4. Kinetic energy.
5. Electrical to heat, kinetic and sound.
6. None.
7. 9%.

USING ENERGY RESOURCES

electrical energy ⇨ sound

Electricical energy is one of the **most convenient forms of energy**. It is **easily converted** into other forms of energy.

FOSSIL FUELS

Coal, oil and gas are called <u>fossil fuels</u>. They are <u>concentrated sources</u> of energy.

- Fossil fuels are formed from <u>plants and animals</u> that died over 100 million years ago.
- When they died they became covered with many layers of <u>mud</u> and <u>earth</u>.
- The resulting <u>large pressures and high temperatures</u> changed them into fossil fuels.
- Because they take millions of years to form these fuels are called <u>non-renewable</u> fuels.
- Once they have been used up they <u>cannot be replaced</u>.

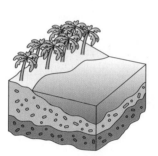

Dead plants and animals are covered with mud and earth.

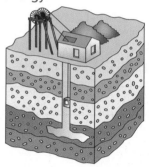

After hundreds of millions of years they have changed into fossil fuels such as coal.

THE PROBLEMS WITH NON-RENEWABLE FUELS
- When any of the fossil fuels are burned they produce <u>carbon dioxide</u>. Increasing the amount of carbon dioxide in the atmosphere causes the temperature of the Earth and its atmosphere to rise. This is called the greenhouse effect.
- When coal and oil are burned they also produce gases that cause <u>acid rain</u>.
- <u>Environmental problems</u> are created by <u>mining</u> and <u>spillage of oil during transport</u>.
- We are using up fossil fuels very quickly and will soon have to find other sources of energy, but we need to start looking <u>now</u>.

THE SOLUTIONS
We need to slow down the rate at which we are using fossil fuels so that they will last longer. There are several ways in which we can do this:
- <u>Reduce petrol consumption</u> by driving smaller cars, using public transport or walking or cycling. We should also develop more efficient car engines.
- <u>Improve the insulation</u> to our homes and factories so less energy is wasted heating them.
- <u>Increase public awareness</u> of how people are wasting energy so that they turn off lights and turn down heating wherever possible.

We also need to look for other sources of energy:
- In the UK some of our electricity is generated by <u>nuclear power stations</u>
- <u>Renewable sources of energy</u> such as wind, waves, tidal, solar, geothermal, biomass and hydroelectric <u>need to be developed</u>. Each of these sources have some advantages and disadvantages. These are described in more detail on pages 30–31.

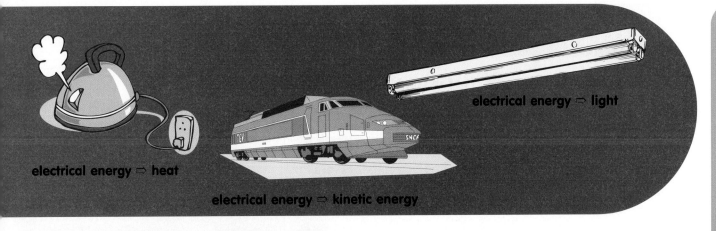

electrical energy ⇨ light

electrical energy ⇨ heat

electrical energy ⇨ kinetic energy

POWER STATIONS

Most of the electrical energy we use at home is generated at <u>power</u> <u>stations</u>. There are several different types of power station but the most common in the UK use <u>coal</u> <u>or</u> <u>gas</u> as their source of energy (fuel).

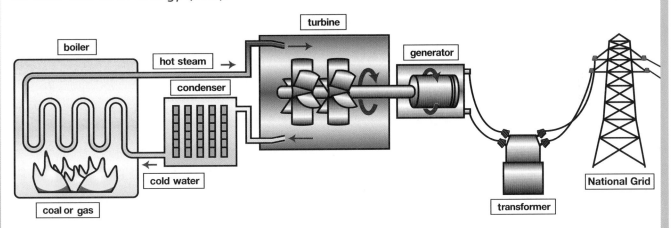

CHEMICAL ENERGY	HEAT ENERGY	KINETIC ENERGY	ELECTRICAL ENERGY

- The fuel is burned to release its <u>energy</u>.
- The <u>heat energy released</u> is used to heat water and turn it into <u>steam</u>.
- The steam <u>turns turbines</u>.
- The turbines <u>turn large generators</u>.
- The <u>generators produce electrical energy</u>.
- The electrical energy is carried to our homes through the <u>National Grid</u>.

Examiner's Top Tip
This is another very popular topic and appears regularly on exam papers. Make sure that you understand the energy changes that take place when electricity is generated at the power station. Also learn the problems that burning fossil fuels create for the atmosphere and the environment.

QUICK TEST

1. **Name three fossil fuels.**

2. **What gas causes the greenhouse effect?**

3. **Which fossil fuels cause acid rain when burned?**

4. **Name one type of environmental damage that might be caused as a result of using fossil fuels in our power stations.**

5. **Why are fossil fuels called non-renewable sources of energy?**

6. **Suggest three ways in which we could make fossil fuels last longer.**

1. Coal, oil and gas.
2. Carbon dioxide.
3. Coal and oil.
4. Oil spillage/global warming/acid rain.
5. They cannot be replaced.
6. More efficient insulation and engines, make more use of alternative sources of energy.

GEOTHERMAL

In regions where the Earth's crust is thin, <u>hot rocks beneath the ground</u> can be used to heat water, turning it into steam. This steam is then used to drive turbines and generate electricity.

+ <u>Renewable</u> source of energy.
+ No pollution and no environmental problems.

– Very few <u>suitable sites</u>.
– <u>High cost</u> of drilling deep into the ground.

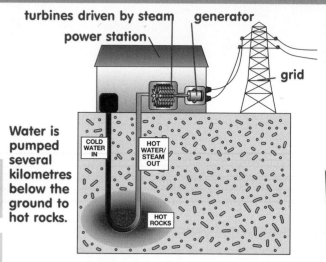

Water is pumped several kilometres below the ground to hot rocks.

Radioactive decay produces heat to warm the rocks and magma chambers close to the surface.

ALTERNATIVE SOURCES OF ENERGY

The energy carried in the Sun's rays is converted directly into electrical energy by solar cells. This then powers the car.

+ = advantages   – = disadvantages

TIDAL POWER

At high tide, water is trapped behind a barrage or dam. When it is released at low tide the <u>gravitational potential energy</u> of the water changes into <u>kinetic energy</u> which then drives turbines and generates electricity.

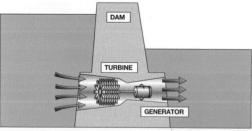

+ <u>Renewable</u> source.
+ <u>Reliable</u>: two tides per day.
+ No atmospheric <u>pollution</u>.
+ <u>Low</u> running costs.

– <u>High</u> initial cost.
– Possible <u>damage to environment</u>, e.g. flooding.
– Obstacle to <u>water transport</u>.

Examiner's Top Tip
Don't waste time memorising the diagrams, but study them and remember the advantages and disadvantages of each resource.

SOLAR ENERGY

The energy carried in the <u>Sun's rays</u> can be converted directly into electricity using solar cells.

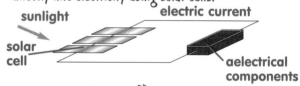

or

The energy carried in the Sun's rays is absorbed by dark coloured panels and used to <u>heat</u> water.

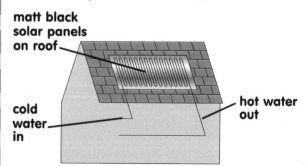

+ No pollution.

– Initially quite <u>expensive</u>.
– May not be so useful in regions where there is <u>limited sunshine</u>.

BIOMASS

The <u>chemical</u> <u>energy</u> stored in 'things that have grown', e.g. wood, can be <u>released</u> <u>by</u> <u>burning</u> it. This energy source can be maintained by growing a succession of trees and then cropping them when they mature.

+ <u>Renewable</u> source of energy.
+ <u>Low-level</u> <u>technology</u>, therefore useful in developing countries.
+ Does not add to the greenhouse effect as the carbon dioxide released by trees and plants when burned was taken from the atmosphere as they grew.

– <u>Large</u> areas of land needed to grow sufficient numbers of trees.

WIND POWER

The kinetic energy of the <u>wind</u> is used to drive turbines and generators.

+ It is a <u>renewable</u> source of energy and therefore will not be exhausted.
+ Has <u>low-level</u> <u>technology</u> and therefore can be used in developing countries.
+ No atmospheric pollution.

– <u>Visual</u> and <u>noise</u> <u>pollution</u>.
– Limited to <u>windy</u> sites.
– No wind, no energy.

HYDROELECTRICITY

The kinetic energy of <u>flowing</u> <u>water</u> is used to drive turbines and generators.

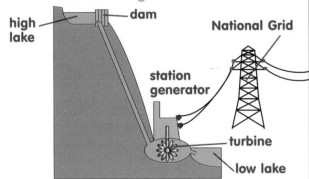

high lake — dam

National Grid

station generator

turbine

low lake

+ <u>Renewable</u> source.
+ Energy can be <u>stored</u> until required.
+ No <u>atmospheric</u> <u>pollution</u>.

– <u>High</u> initial cost.
– <u>High</u> cost to environment, e.g. flooding, loss of habitat.

WAVE POWER

The <u>rocking</u> <u>motion</u> of the waves is used to generate electricity.

simple wave machine

the energy in the water waves make this machine rock

this motion is then used to generate electricity

+ <u>Renewable</u> source.
+ No atmospheric pollution.
+ Useful for isolated islands.

– <u>High</u> initial cost.
– Visual pollution.
– <u>Poor</u> <u>energy</u> <u>capture</u>: large area of machines needed even for small energy return.

QUICK TEST

1. Name three ways in which water could be used as an energy resource.
2. Name two energy resources which may pollute the environment visually.
3. Name two energy resources which could be easily used and maintained in developing countries.
4. Name two energy resources whose capture require a suitable site that might be rare.
5. Name one energy resource whose capture might cause an audible pollution.

1. Hydroelectricity, tidal, wave.
2. Wind, waves.
3. Wind, biomass.
4. Geothermal, tidal.
5. Wind.

CONDUCTION THROUGH SOLIDS

- After five or 10 minutes the whole length of this metal rod is hot. <u>Heat</u> has been transferred along the rod by <u>conduction</u>.

conduction

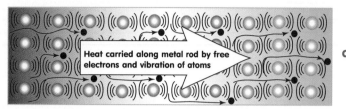

hot

Heat carried along metal rod by free electrons and vibration of atoms

cold

Which metal is the best conductor?

A marble is stuck on the end of each bar with wax. Heat is conducted along all the bars and melts the wax. The first marble falls from the bar that is the best conductor.

- The <u>atoms</u> at the hot end <u>vibrate</u>. Free electrons collide with these atoms and gain energy. The motion of these energetic electrons transfers energy to the cooler end of the rod.

All <u>metals</u> are good conductors of heat because:
- their <u>atoms</u> are <u>packed</u> <u>close</u> <u>together</u>.
- they have <u>large</u> <u>numbers</u> <u>of</u> <u>free</u> <u>electrons</u>.

<u>Non-metals</u> are usually poor conductors of heat because:
- their <u>atoms</u> are <u>further</u> <u>apart</u>.
- there are <u>fewer</u> <u>free</u> <u>electrons</u>.

HEAT TRANSFER

Heat will flow when there is a temperature difference between two places. It will flow from the hotter to the cooler place. There are three main methods by which it can do this. These are <u>conduction</u>, <u>convection</u> and <u>radiation</u>.

INSULATING THE HOME

- This diagram shows how heat may escape from a house that has not been insulated.

10% through windows, reduced by installing double glazing.

25% through roof, reduced by putting insulation into loft.

25% through walls, reduced by having cavity wall insulation.

25% through gaps and cracks around doors and windows, reduced by fitting draft excluders.

15% through floor, reduced by fitting carpets and underlay.

CONDUCTION THROUGH LIQUIDS AND GASES

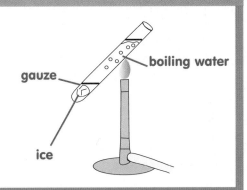

- **Water**, like most liquids, is a **poor conductor of heat** – So poor that it is possible to have frozen water and boiling water just a few centimetres apart.
- **Gases** are **worse conductors than liquids**. They are in fact excellent **insulators**. An **insulator** is a material that **does not allow** heat to travel through it easily by **conduction**.
- It is **impossible** for heat to travel by **conduction** through a **vacuum** as it contains no particles.

CONDUCTORS AND INSULATORS

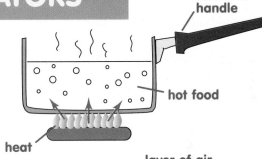

- A good saucepan is made from materials that are conductors and insulators. The base and sides of the pan are made of metal so that heat is easily conducted from the flame to the food. The handle is made from an insulator so that it does not become too hot to hold.

- Glass fibre is an excellent insulator because it contains large amounts of trapped air. It is placed in the loft to reduce heat loss.

- It is the layer of air trapped between the two panes of glass that make double glazing an excellent method of reducing heat loss from a house.

- The metal blade of a knife conducts heat away from your fingers and so feels cold. Plastics are good insulators so the plastic handle does not conduct heat away and so feels warm.

Woven materials, e.g. wool and cotton, contain trapped air and are excellent insulators.

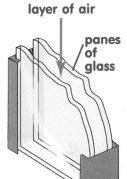

QUICK TEST

1. Give one example and one use of a good conductor.
2. Give one example and one use of an insulator.
3. Why do metals always feel cold?
4. Why are plastic place mats put under hot plates?
5. What is double glazing? How does it provide good insulation?
6. Suggest five methods by which you could reduce the heat escaping from your house.

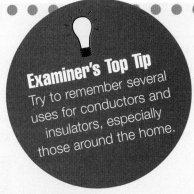

Examiner's Top Tip
Try to remember several uses for conductors and insulators, especially those around the home.

1. All metals, e.g. a saucepan.
2. Plastic, e.g. a saucepan handle.
3. They conduct the heat away from your body quickly.
4. They prevent heat from the plates damaging the tabletop.
5. Two panes of glass with a narrow gap. The gap contains air which is a good insulator.
6. Double glazing, loft insulation, cavity wall insulation, carpets and underlay, draught excluders.

CONVECTION CURRENTS

4. Fluid cools, becomes more dense and falls.

3. Heat is carried to all parts of the tube by convection current.

2. Fluid expands, becomes less dense and rises.

1. Liquid/gas is warmed.

- After several minutes all the liquid/gas in the container has been warmed, i.e. heat has been transferred to all parts.
- This <u>circular</u> <u>movement</u> <u>of</u> <u>fluid</u> is called a <u>convection</u> <u>current</u>.
- Convection cannot take place in a solid. The particles of a solid are unable to move position.

HEATING A ROOM BY CONVECTION

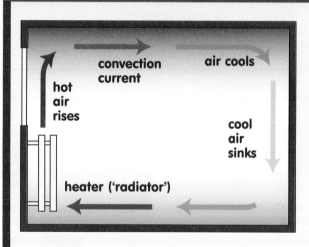

convection current

air cools

hot air rises

cool air sinks

heater ('radiator')

Radiators are badly named. Most of the heat they give to a room is <u>transferred</u> not by <u>radiation</u> but by <u>convection</u>.

Examiner's Top Tip
Remember that the hottest region of a liquid or gas is usually near the top.

CONVECTION CURRENTS

CONVECTION CURRENTS IN OVENS AND FRIDGES

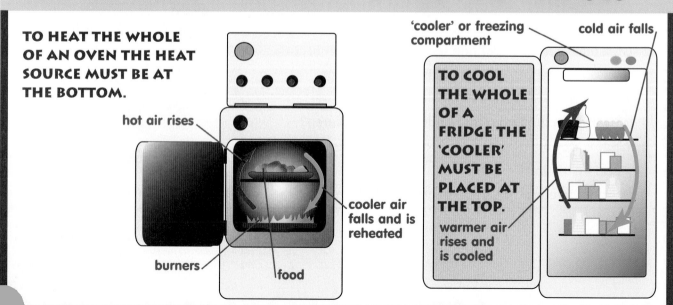

TO HEAT THE WHOLE OF AN OVEN THE HEAT SOURCE MUST BE AT THE BOTTOM.

hot air rises

cooler air falls and is reheated

burners

food

'cooler' or freezing compartment

cold air falls

TO COOL THE WHOLE OF A FRIDGE THE 'COOLER' MUST BE PLACED AT THE TOP.

warmer air rises and is cooled

DOMESTIC HOT WATER SYSTEM

- <u>Warm</u> <u>water</u> in the boiler rises and enters the top of the hot-water tank.
- <u>Cool</u> <u>water</u> is taken from <u>bottom</u> <u>of</u> <u>the</u> <u>hot-water</u> <u>tank</u> and <u>reheated</u>.
- Water removed through the taps is replaced with water from the cold-water tank.

A liquid or gas is warmed. The <u>fluid</u> <u>expands</u>, <u>becomes</u> <u>less</u> <u>dense</u> <u>and</u> <u>rises</u>, carrying its extra energy with it. The warmer fluid is replaced with cooler fluid, which is then heated.

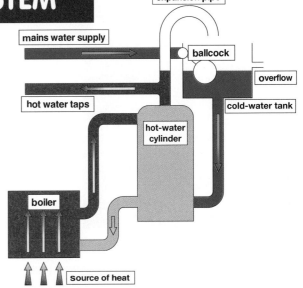

CARRY HEAT AROUND

CONVECTION

SEA BREEZES

During the day the land is hotter than the sea and an on-shore breeze is set up.

Day

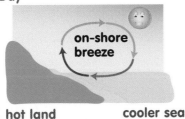

hot land   cooler sea

During the night the sea is warmer than the land and an offshore breeze is set up.

Night

cold land   warmer sea

Examiner's Top Tip
It is a common mistake to write that heat rises. It is better to say that when warmed a liquid or gas becomes less dense and rises, taking heat energy with it.

QUICK TEST

1. Transfer of heat by convection can only take place in .... and ....
2. Transfer of heat by convection <u>cannot</u> take place in ....
3. Why is a radiator badly named?
4. Where should the freezing compartment of a fridge be placed so it cools the whole of a fridge?
5. Where in a hot-water tank is the hottest water?
6. In which direction will a sea breeze blow at midday during a hot summer?

6. Hot air will rise from the beach so an onshore breeze will blow.
5. The hot, less dense water is at the top of the tank.
4. The cooler should be at the top of the compartment as this is where the air is warmest.
3. Because most heat is transferred from a radiator by convection not by radiation.
2. Solids.
1. Liquids, gases.

HEAT FROM THE SUN

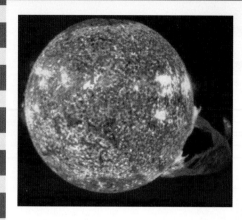

Heat travels from the <u>Sun to the Earth as waves</u> (radiation). There are no particles between the Sun and the Earth's atmosphere so heat cannot travel by conduction or convection.

ABSORPTION OR REFLECTION

When waves strike an object they can be a) <u>absorbed</u> or b) <u>reflected</u>.

Objects with <u>dark, rough surfaces absorb most of the radiation</u> and become hotter.

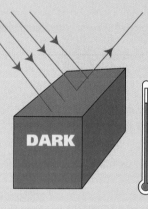

DARK

Objects with <u>light-coloured, shiny surfaces reflect most of the radiation</u> and will remain cooler.

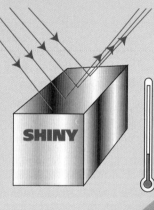

SHINY

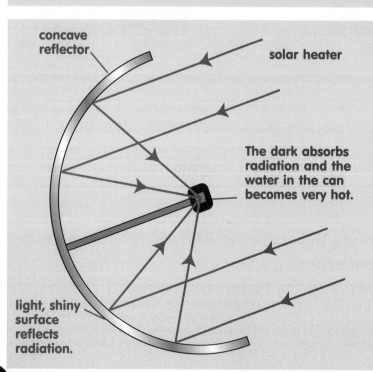

concave reflector

solar heater

The dark absorbs radiation and the water in the can becomes very hot.

light, shiny surface reflects radiation.

SOLAR HEATER

The light-coloured surface of the curved mirror reflects the heat. The dark matt surface of the can of water absorbs the heat.

EMITTING RADIATION

Warm objects give off or emit <u>heat</u> <u>radiation</u>.
(How do you know a radiator is hot
without touching it?)

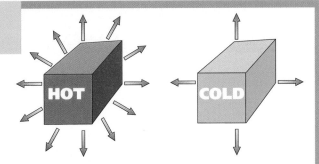

Objects with <u>dark</u>, <u>matt</u> <u>surfaces</u> give off lots of radiation, i.e. they are <u>good</u> <u>emitters</u>.
Objects with <u>light</u>, <u>shiny</u> <u>surfaces</u> give off less radiation, i.e. they are <u>poor</u> <u>emitters</u>.

after 20 minutes

poor emitter   good emitter

After 20 minutes the water in the black teapot is cooler, because it has emitted more radiation.

RADIATION

This is the transfer of heat by waves.

QUICK TEST

1. Name three methods by which heat can travel.

2. How does heat travel from the Sun to the Earth?

3. What two things might happen when heat radiation strikes an object?

4. What kind of surface is an object that is a good absorber of radiation likely to have?

5. What kind of surface is an object that is a very poor absorber of radiation likely to have?

6. Why do some people in hot countries wear light-coloured clothes?

7. What kind of surface is an object that is a good emitter of radiation likely to have?

8. What kind of surface is an object that is a poor emitter of radiation likely to have?

9. What colour should a radiator be painted so that it can warm a room quickly?

9. Black.
8. Light-coloured and smooth.
7. Dark and rough.
6. Light-coloured clothes will reflect most radiation and absorb only a little. The wearer will therefore remain cool.
5. Light-coloured and smooth.
4. Dark and rough.
3. It is either absorbed or reflected.
2. Radiation.
1. Conduction, convection and radiation.

EXAM QUESTIONS — Use the questions to test your progress. Check your answers on page 94.

1. Name a device which changes:
   a) electrical energy into kinetic energy...
   b) kinetic energy into electrical energy...
   c) light energy into electrical energy...

2. What kind of energy is electrical energy changed into by:
   a) a loudspeaker...
   b) a battery charger...

3. What kind of energy does a clockwork toy gain as it is being wound up?

   ....

4. What kind of energy does a lift have when it has stopped on the top floor of a building?

   ....

5. Name the main method of heat transfer in each of the following:
   a) Sun to Earth...
   b) radiator to room...
   c) cooker hot-plate to food in saucepan...

6. a) Explain what is meant by the phrase 'renewable source of energy'...............................
   b) Name three renewable sources of energy...

   ....

7. Most of the energy used by industrialised countries comes from burning fossil fuels.
   a) Name three fossil fuels...
   b) Why are fossil fuels called non-renewable sources of energy?...............................
   c) Name a fuel which is renewable...

8. Suggest three ways of reducing the rate at which fossil fuels are used.

   ....

9. What steps could be taken to reduce heat-loss from a house.

   ....

10. The diagram (right) shows the flow of heat through double glazing.
    a) Explain why double glazing is a better form of insulation than a single
    pane of thick glass.
    ....

    b) By which method can energy easily travel through double glazing?
    ....

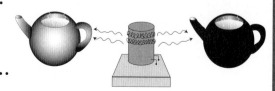

11. The diagram (below) shows two teapots containing equal amounts of water being
    warmed by a radiant heater.
    a) What is the temperature of the water before the heater is turned on?

    ....

    b) What happens to the temperature of the water in the black
    teapot compared with the water in the white teapot?

    ....

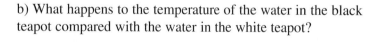

    c) Why are houses in hot countries often painted white?

    ....

12. The diagram (right) shows how a convection current is created on the coast.
Match the descriptions 1, 2, 3 and 4 with the positions A, B, C and D.
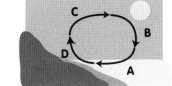
   1. Air cools, contracts becomes more dense and falls......................
   2. Land warms up quickly and heats the air above it.......................
   3. Cooler air rushes in to take the place of the warmer rising air.............
   4. Air that has been warmed is less dense and so rises.....................

13. The diagram (right) shows a solar panel.
   a) Why are the pipes and the collector plate painted black?..............
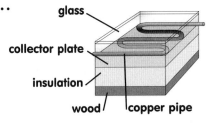
....

   b) Why are the pipes and plate placed on a piece of insulation?

....

   c) Why is the panel covered with glass?

....

14. A crane uses 500 J of electrical energy to give a crate 300 J of gravitational
potential energy. Calculate the efficiency of the crane.

....

15. An electric light bulb is 20% efficient. If 200 J of electrical energy enters the bulb how much light energy
is produced?

....

16. The table below list some ways in which the heating bills for a house could be reduced.

Method	Initial cost	Yearly saving	Payback time
Hot-water jacket	£10	£10	A
Loft insulation	£240	£60	B
Double glazing	£3600	£60	C

   a) Calculate the payback time A, B and C for each of these methods.

....

   b) Which method is the most cost-effective?

....

17. The diagram (right) shows a hydroelectric power station.
   a) What kind of energy does the water possess in the top lake?
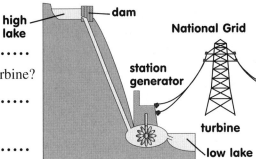

....

   b) What kind of energy does the water possess as it enters the turbine?

....

   c) Explain how surplus energy could be stored until it is needed.

....

   d) Calculate the efficiency of a turbine which transfers 800 kJ of energy into
600 kJ of electrical energy every second.

....

How did you do?

1–5	correct	................start again
6–10	correct	............getting there
11–14	corrrect	............good work
15–17	correct	............excellent

WAVES... CARRY ENERGY FROM PLACE TO PLACE

THE RIPPLE TANK

This apparatus lets us see all the main properties of waves. The small motor makes the rod vibrate, the rod creates ripples and the lamp helps us see the wave pattern on the floor.

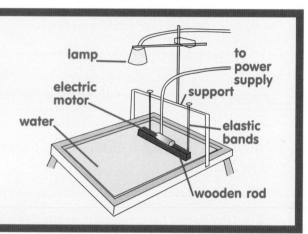

WAVE PATTERNS SEEN WITH THE RIPPLE TANK

LOW FREQUENCY/ LONG WAVELENGTH

low frequency — electric motor
— vibrating rod

long wavelength

HIGHER FREQUENCY/ SHORTER WAVELENGTH

higher frequency

shorter wavelength

- If the rod is made to vibrate more quickly, the frequency of the waves increases but their wavelength decreases.

i = angle of incidence
r = angle of reflection

REFLECTION
- When the waves strike a plane barrier, they are reflected at the same angle i.e. <u>angle of incidence</u> = <u>angle of reflection</u>.

REFLECTION FROM CURVED SURFACES
- When the waves strike a <u>concave</u> or <u>converging</u> surface they <u>reflect</u> and <u>come together</u> or <u>converge</u>.
- When the waves strike a <u>convex</u> or <u>diverging</u> surface they <u>reflect</u> and <u>spread out</u> or <u>diverge</u>.

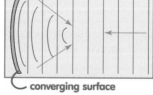

converging surface

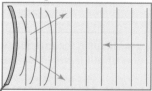

diverging surface

POINT SOURCES
- If the vibrating rod is replaced by a point source, e.g. a small ball, its vibrations create circular waves.

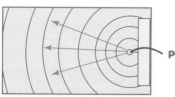

point source

THE IMPORTANT BITS!

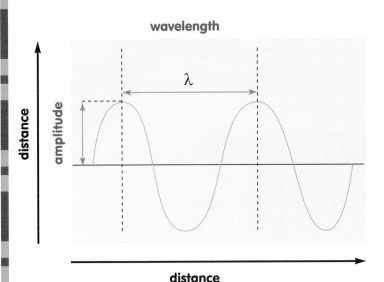

wavelength

λ

amplitude

distance

distance

- The distance from the peak of one wave to the peak of the next wave is called the <u>wavelength</u>(λ).
- The maximum height of the wave from the undisturbed position is called the <u>amplitude</u>.
- The <u>frequency</u> of a wave is the number of waves produced each second by the source, e.g. a frequency of 5 Hz means five waves are made each second by the source.

Examiner's Top Tip
This is a very important topic. Understanding the basic properties of waves will help you understand the behaviour of light waves, sound waves and seismic waves… so concentrate really hard on this spread!

TRANSVERSE WAVES AND LONGITUDINAL WAVES

- There are two main types of waves:

1. A <u>transverse</u> <u>wave</u> has vibrations <u>across</u> or at right angles to the direction in which the wave is moving. Examples of transverse waves include <u>light</u> <u>waves</u> and <u>surface</u> <u>water</u> <u>waves</u>.

wave direction

vibrations

2. A <u>longitudinal</u> <u>wave</u> has vibrations that move along or parallel to the direction in which the wave is moving. <u>Sound waves</u> are longitudinal waves.

wave direction

vibrations

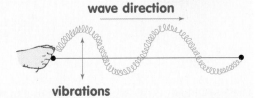

QUICK TEST

1. What do waves carry from place to place?
2. Draw a wave and mark on it the wavelength and the amplitude.
3. Explain the phrase 'a wave has a frequency of 25 Hz'.
4. What is a transverse wave? Give one example of a transverse wave.
5. What is a longitudinal wave? Give one example of a longitudinal wave.
6. If a wave strikes a plane barrier, it is reflected so that the angle of ……….. is ……… to the angle of ……….. .

sound wave. 6. Incidence, equal, reflection.

direction in which the wave is moving; light waves. 5. A wave in which the vibrations are along the direction in which the wave is moving;

1. Energy. 2. ~~amplitude~~ amplitude. 3. The wave source creates 25 waves each second. 4. A wave in which the vibrations are across the

REFLECTION AND REFRACTION

SEEING OBJECTS

- We see <u>luminous</u> <u>objects</u> such as fires, light bulbs and stars because some of the light they <u>emit</u> enters our eyes.
- We see non-luminous objects because some of the light they <u>reflect</u> enters our eyes.

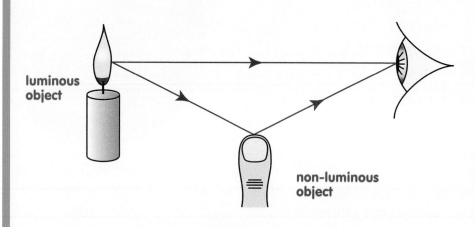

luminous object

non-luminous object

PLANE AND DIFFUSION REFLECTION

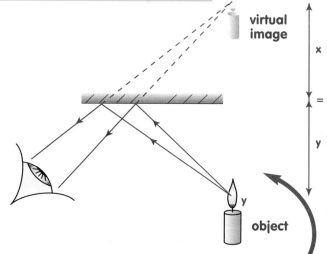

virtual image

object

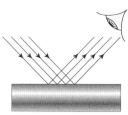

shiny surface

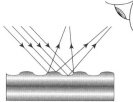

matt or rough surface

- **All the rays are reflected in the same direction. Lots of light enters our eyes so the surface looks <u>shiny</u> <u>or</u> <u>glossy</u>.**

- **Because the light is <u>scattered</u>, only a little of it enters our eyes so the surface appears <u>dull</u> <u>or</u> <u>matt</u>.**

THE IMAGE CREATED BY A PLANE MIRROR
The image of an object is:
- <u>upright</u>
- the <u>same</u> <u>size</u> as the object
- the <u>same</u> <u>distance</u> behind the mirror as the object is in front of it
- <u>laterally</u> <u>inverted</u>, i.e. the left is seen on the left and the right is seen on the right
- a <u>virtual</u> <u>image</u>, i.e. it cannot be formed on a screen placed behind the mirror.

REFLECTION FROM A PLANE MIRROR

- When a ray of light strikes a plane mirror it is reflected so that the <u>angle</u> <u>of</u> <u>incidence</u> is equal to the <u>angle</u> <u>of</u> <u>reflection</u>. The angles are always measured from the normal.

SIMPLE PERISCOPE

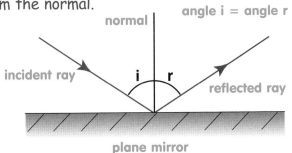

angle i = angle r

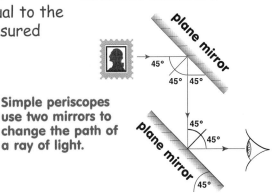

Simple periscopes use two mirrors to change the path of a ray of light.

REFRACTION

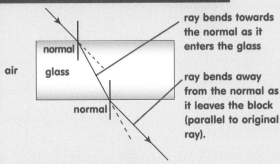

ray bends towards the normal as it enters the glass

ray bends away from the normal as it leaves the block (parallel to original ray).

- When a ray of light enters a glass block it <u>slows</u> <u>down</u> and bends <u>towards</u> <u>the</u> <u>normal</u>.
- This change of direction is called <u>refraction</u>.
- When the ray emerges from the block it <u>speeds</u> <u>up</u> and bends <u>away</u> <u>from</u> <u>the</u> <u>normal</u>.
- If the ray meets the surface at <u>90°</u>, it <u>does</u> <u>not</u> <u>change</u> <u>direction</u> but there is no change in speed.

NO CHANGE IN DIRECTION

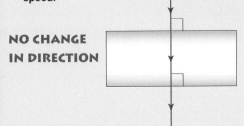

STRANGE EFFECTS OF REFRACTION

This pencil looks bent because the rays of light are <u>refracted</u> <u>as</u> <u>they</u> <u>emerge</u> <u>from</u> <u>the</u> <u>water</u>. This swimming pool is deeper than it appears. This is also caused by refraction.

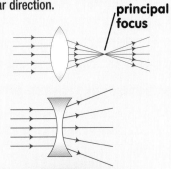

pencil

beaker

water

apparent depth of swimming pool

air

ray is refracted

water

real depth of swimming pool

i = image
o = object

LENSES

Lenses are <u>specially</u> <u>shaped</u> <u>pieces</u> <u>of</u> <u>glass</u> <u>or</u> <u>plastic</u>, which are used to refract light in a particular direction.

- A converging lens refracts the light so that rays of light are brought together (<u>converge</u>).

principal focus

- A diverging lens refracts light so that rays of light are made to spread out (<u>diverge</u>).

QUICK TEST

1. What is a luminous object?
2. The angle of incidence is equal to the angle of ....
3. Describe the image that is created by a plane mirror.
4. What happens to a ray of light when it is refracted?
5. What causes a ray of light to be refracted?

5. The change in speed as the ray crosses the boundary between two media.
4. It changes direction.
3. Upright, same size, same distance behind mirror and virtual.
2. Reflection.
1. One which gives off its own light.

DISPERSION AND TOTAL INTERNAL REFLECTION

DISPERSION

- **White light is a <u>mixture</u> of <u>coloured lights</u>.**
- **When white light travels through a <u>prism</u>, the different colours are <u>refracted</u> by different amounts. This is called <u>dispersion</u>.**
- **A <u>band</u> of <u>colours</u> called a <u>spectrum</u> is produced.**
- **The colours of the spectrum always appear in the same order: <u>r</u>ed, <u>o</u>range, <u>y</u>ellow, <u>g</u>reen, <u>b</u>lue, <u>i</u>ndigo and <u>v</u>iolet.**

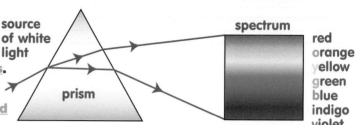

source of white light

prism

spectrum

red
orange
yellow
green
blue
indigo
violet

Easy to remember: Richard Of York Gave Battle In Vain.

TOTAL INTERNAL REFLECTION

- The inner surface of a glass block can sometimes behave like a mirror. This is called <u>total internal reflection</u>.
- Total internal reflection happens if the ray strikes the inside surface of the glass at an angle greater than the <u>critical angle</u>.
- If the angle of incidence is small, the ray is refracted as usual.
- If the angle is large, total internal reflection takes place.
- Total internal reflection only occurs when light travels from a more optically dense material into a less optically dense material (e.g. glass to air).

Examiner's Top Tip
When revising any topic about light, be sure to practise drawing the ray diagrams using a ruler and pencil.

If angle i is less than the critical angle the ray is refracted and passes out of the glass. A small amount is reflected.

air glass weak reflection
i

If angle i is greater than the critical angle the ray is totally internally reflected.

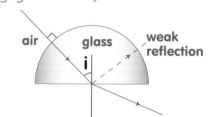

no refraction
air glass
i

If angle i equals the critical angle c the ray emerges along the edge of the glass block.

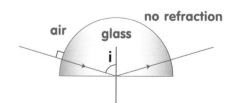

weak reflection
c

TOTAL INTERNAL REFLECTION IN PRISMS

TURNING A RAY THROUGH 90°
This is used in periscopes.

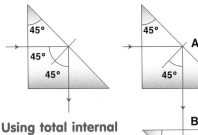

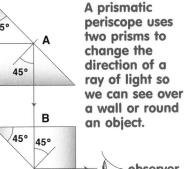

A prismatic periscope uses two prisms to change the direction of a ray of light so we can see over a wall or round an object.

observer

Using total internal reflection, a single glass prism can turn a ray of light through 90°. Glass has a critical angle of 42°.

TURNING A RAY THROUGH 180°
This is used in bicycle reflectors and binoculars.

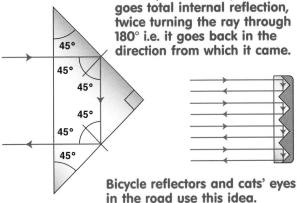

In this prism the ray undergoes total internal reflection, twice turning the ray through 180° i.e. it goes back in the direction from which it came.

Bicycle reflectors and cats' eyes in the road use this idea.

OPTICAL FIBRES AND LIGHT PIPES

- An optical fibre has a <u>high-density glass</u> <u>for</u> <u>its core</u> and a <u>less dense glass</u> <u>as an outer coating</u>.
- The fibre is so narrow that light entering at one end will always strike the boundary between the two glasses at an angle <u>greater than the critical angle</u>.
- It will therefore undergo a <u>series of total internal reflections</u> before emerging at the far end of the fibre.
- Fibres can be bundled together to make <u>light pipes</u>.
- Because these pipes are flexible we can use them to see and bend light around corners.
- Optical fibres are now used to carry signals, e.g. cable TV.

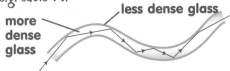

less dense glass

more dense glass

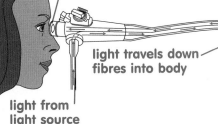

lens creates image of inside of body

light returns from inside body

light travels down fibres into body

light from light source

THE ENDOSCOPE
- Used by surgeons to see inside the body.
- Light travels down one set of fibres and is reflected back through another set.

Examiner's Top Tip
Questions about optical fibres are very popular as a lot of new technology makes use of them. Learn this section thoroughly.

QUICK TEST

1. What is a spectrum?
2. How is a spectrum produced?
3. What two conditions are needed for total internal reflection to occur?
4. Name an optical instrument that uses two prisms to change the direction of rays of light.
5. Explain how a prism in a bicycle reflector turns light through 180°.
6. Give one use of an optical fibre.

1. A band of colours.
2. Through the dispersion of light.
3. The rays must be travelling from a more dense to a less dense medium, and at an angle greater than the critical angle.
4. A periscope.
5. The light is totally internally reflected twice inside the prism.
6. Endoscope, cable TV.

THE ELECTROMAGNETIC SPECTRUM

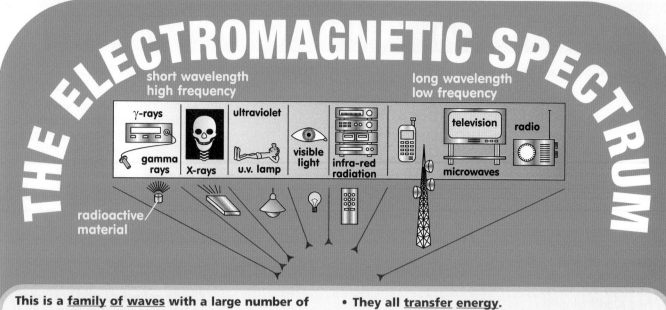

short wavelength
high frequency

long wavelength
low frequency

γ-rays | gamma rays | X-rays | ultraviolet | u.v. lamp | visible light | infra-red radiation | microwaves | television | radio

radioactive material

This is a **family** **of** **waves** with a large number of **common** **properties**:
- They are all able to **travel** **through** **a** **vacuum**.
- They all travel at the **same** **speed** through a vacuum, i.e. the speed of light (300 000 000 m/s).
- They are all **transverse** **waves**.

- They all **transfer** **energy**.
- They can all be **reflected**, **refracted** and **diffracted**. Some of the **properties** of these waves **change** as the **wavelength** **and** **frequency** changes. The family is therefore divided into seven smaller groups.

RADIO WAVES

- Radio waves are used for **communicating** **over** **large** **distances**.
- Short wavelength radio waves are used for television broadcasting and FM radio.
- Longer wavelength radio waves are used for traditional AM radio.

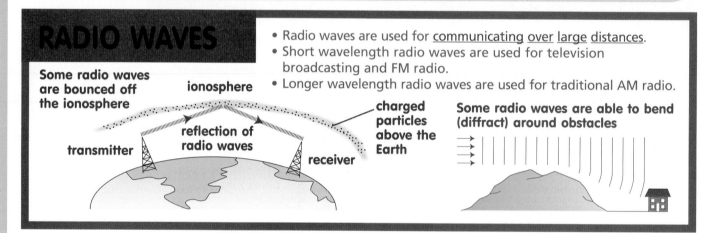

Some radio waves are bounced off the ionosphere

ionosphere

charged particles above the Earth

transmitter

reflection of radio waves

receiver

Some radio waves are able to bend (diffract) around obstacles

MICROWAVES

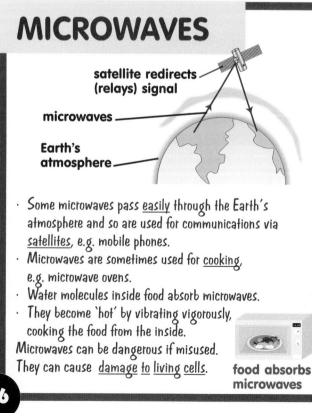

satellite redirects (relays) signal

microwaves

Earth's atmosphere

- Some microwaves pass **easily** through the Earth's atmosphere and so are used for communications via **satellites**, e.g. mobile phones.
- Microwaves are sometimes used for **cooking**, e.g. microwave ovens.
- Water molecules inside food absorb microwaves.
- They become 'hot' by vibrating vigorously, cooking the food from the inside.
Microwaves can be dangerous if misused. They can cause **damage** **to** **living** **cells**.

food absorbs microwaves

INFRA-RED WAVES (HEAT RADIATION)

Warm objects give off infra-red waves which our skin can detect

- Infra-red waves are **given** **out** **by** **all** **warm** **objects**.
- Our skin is sensitive to infra-red waves.
- Overexposure causes **sunburn** but not tanning.
- Infra-red waves are used to 'see **in** **the** **dark**'. Special 'heat-seeking' cameras **create** **images** of objects using the **infra-red** **waves** **they** **are** **emitting**. These are often used by the emergency services to detect people trapped in collapsed buildings or lost in mountains or on moors.
- **Remote** **controls** for TVs, radios, etc. use infra-red waves to carry instructions.

Infra-red waves carry the instruction from the remote to the TV

VISIBLE LIGHT

We use visible light to see

- *Our eyes make use of waves from this part of the spectrum to allow us to <u>see</u>.*
- *It is the one part of the electromagnetic spectrum to which our <u>eyes</u> <u>are</u> <u>sensitive</u>.*
- *Visible light is also used to carry messages down <u>optical</u> <u>fibres</u>.*

ULTRAVIOLET

- Ultraviolet waves are <u>emitted</u> by the Sun.
- They cause our skins to tan.
- Over-exposure to ultraviolet waves <u>can lead to skin cancer</u>.
- Certain chemicals <u>fluoresce</u> (<u>glow</u>) when exposed to ultraviolet waves.
- Words written with security markers are only visible in ultraviolet light.

The inside of the tube has a special coating

When turned on, ultraviolet waves are emitted inside the tube

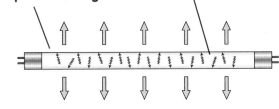

When the ultraviolet waves strike this coating they are absorbed and visible light is emitted

X-RAYS

X-rays are used to look inside the body at the bones

- X-rays have a very <u>short wavelength</u> and a very <u>high frequency</u>.
- They are <u>highly penetrating</u>.
- They are used to look for damaged bones inside the body.
- Overexposure can cause cancer. Radiographers therefore stand behind <u>lead screens</u> or wear <u>lead aprons</u> to <u>prevent overexposure</u> because X-rays cannot penetrate lead.

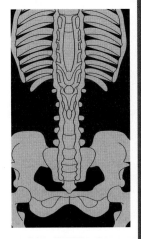

GAMMA RAYS (γ RAYS)

- These are <u>very penetrating</u> waves which are emitted by some <u>radioactive materials</u> (see page 84).
- They can be used to kill harmful bacteria, e.g. to sterilise surgical equipment.
- If used correctly they can be used to kill certain kinds of cancer. This procedure is called <u>radiotherapy</u>.
- Incorrect exposure or dosage can damage living cells and <u>cause cancer</u>.

QUICK TEST

1. Name two properties the waves fo the electromagnetic spectrum have in common.
2. Name two features of these waves that change as we move from group to group.
3. Name three types of waves that can be used for communications.
4. Name two types of waves that can be used for cooking.
5. Name three types of waves that might cause cancer.
6. Name one type of wave that can be used to treat cancer.
7. Name two types of waves that can be sensed by human beings.
8. Name one source of gamma rays.

1. They are all transverse and travel through a vacuum at the same speed.
2. Wavelength and frequency.
3. Radio, microwave, visible.
4. Infra-red, microwaves.
5. Ultraviolet, X-ray and gamma.
6. Gamma.
7. Visible light and infrared.
8. Radioactive materials.

SOUNDS

All sounds begin with an <u>object</u> that is <u>vibrating</u>.
These vibrations travel outwards from the source.
If they strike someone's <u>eardrum</u>, they may be heard.

PITCH AND FREQUENCY

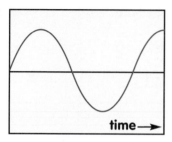

low-pitched sound

- Large objects <u>vibrate slowly</u> and produce just a few waves each second. These waves have a <u>low frequency</u> and produce <u>low-pitched sounds</u>.

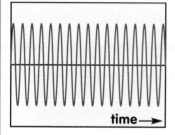

high-pitched sound

- Small objects vibrate quickly and produce lots of waves each second. These waves have a <u>high frequency</u> and produce <u>high-pitched sounds</u>.
- We measure the <u>frequency</u> of a wave or its source in <u>hertz</u> (<u>Hz</u>). An object which <u>vibrates once every second</u> and produces <u>one complete wave every second</u> has a <u>frequency of 1 Hz</u>.

Examiner's Top Tip
When reading this section keep referring back to the basic wave properties on pages 40–41. Remember most of what you have read there is also true for sound waves.

LOUDNESS

- Objects that vibrate with <u>large amplitudes</u> produce <u>loud sounds</u>.

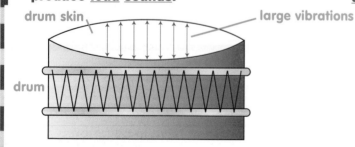

drum skin — large vibrations

drum

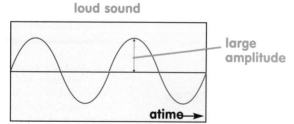

loud sound

large amplitude

atime→

- Objects that have <u>small vibrations</u> produce <u>quiet sounds</u>.

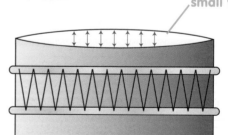

small vibrations

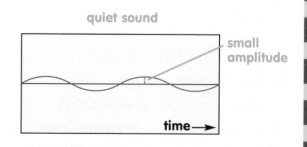

quiet sound

small amplitude

time→

WHAT IS A SOUND WAVE?

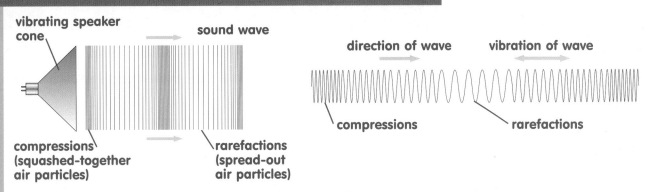

- A vibrating object pushes against air particles creating a <u>compression</u>.
- As it moves in the opposite direction, it creates a <u>region of spread-out particles</u> called a <u>rarefaction</u>.
- As the object continues to vibrate, it creates <u>alternate regions of compressions and rarefactions</u> travelling out from the source. This is a <u>sound wave</u>.

SPEED OF SOUND

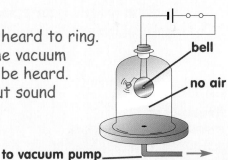

- This is the speed at which the waves move away from the source.
- In air, the speed of sound is approximately 340 m/s.
- This is much lower than the speed of light (approximately 300 000 000 m/s), which is why we often see an event before we hear it, e.g. thunder and lightning.
- A plane which travels faster than sound is described as being <u>supersonic</u>.
- The particles in solids and liquids are much closer together than those in gases, and sound travels through them more quickly, e.g. the speed of sound in water is approximately 1500 m/s.

THE BELL JAR EXPERIMENT

Is there anything a sound wave cannot travel through?

- When the bell (right) is turned on, it can be seen and heard to ring.
- When all the air has been removed from the jar by the vacuum pump, the bell can be seen to be ringing but it cannot be heard.
- Conclusion: light waves can travel through a vacuum but sound waves cannot.

QUICK TEST

1. All sounds begin with an object, that is ....
2. A large vibrating object will produce a .... sound.
3. A small vibrating object will produce a .... sound.
4. A sound wave consists of alternate regions where particles are packed close together or spread apart. These regions are called .... and ....
5. What does the word supersonic mean?
6. Is the speed of sound in a solid faster or slower than the speed of sound in air?
7. What can a sound wave not travel through? Explain your answer.

7. A vacuum. It contains no particles to vibrate.
6. Faster.
5. Faster than the speed of sound.
4. Compressions and rarefactions.
3. High-pitched.
2. Low-pitched.
1. Vibrating.

ECHOES AND HEARING

ECHOES

- When sound waves strike a hard surface they are <u>reflected</u>. This reflected sound is called an <u>echo</u>.
- Ships use echoes to find the depth of the ocean beneath them. An <u>echo-sounder</u> emits sound waves down towards the seabed. When the waves strike the seabed, they are reflected back up to the surface. A sound detector 'listens' for the echo.
- The deeper the ocean the longer it is before the echo is heard. Sound waves used in this way are called <u>SONAR</u>. This stands for <u>SO</u>und <u>N</u>avigation <u>A</u>nd <u>R</u>anging.
- Fishing boats often use sonar to detect shoals of fish. If an echo is heard sooner than expected it is likely that the wave has been reflected from a shoal of fish swimming beneath the boat.

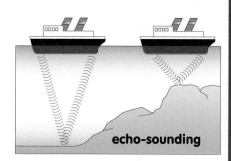

echo-sounding

HEARING RANGE

- An average person can only hear sounds that have a frequency above 20 Hz but below 20 000 Hz. This band of frequencies is called our <u>hearing range</u>.
- Hearing ranges do vary slightly from person to person but in general as we get older our hearing range becomes narrower.
- Sounds that have a frequency which is too high for the human ear to detect are called <u>ultrasounds</u>.
- Ultrasounds can be heard by some animals.
- <u>Dog whistles</u> produce notes we cannot detect but can be heard by a dog.

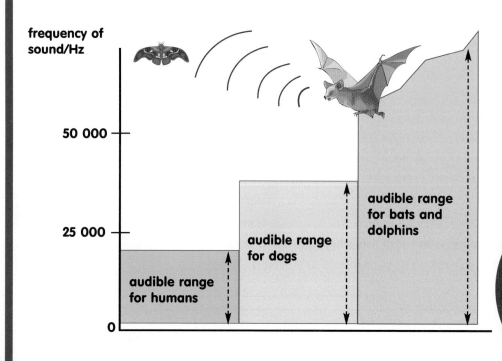

Examiner's Top Tip
When you read an exam question look at the number of marks it is worth. If it is worth three marks try to write three facts.

USES OF ULTRASOUND

- <u>Bats</u> emit ultrasounds and then listen for echoes. Their brains are able to process the reflected waves and use them for <u>navigating</u> <u>and</u> <u>for</u> <u>detecting prey</u>.

- <u>Ultrasonic</u> <u>scanning</u> is carried out in hospitals to monitor the progress of unborn babies in the mother's womb. The waves are emitted by a <u>probe</u> which is placed against the mother's abdomen. Some of the waves are reflected by the foetus. The <u>reflected</u> <u>waves</u> are detected and then <u>processed</u> by a computer which then produces an image of the foetus on a monitor. Ultrasounds do this task far better than X-rays as they do not expose the unborn baby to harmful radiation.

- <u>Ultrasonic</u> <u>waves</u> are also used by industry. They are used to <u>clean</u> very delicate pieces of apparatus without having to take them apart and as part of <u>quality</u> <u>control</u> procedures for certain products, e.g. metal castings.

Ultrasounds are passed through a casting. <u>Internal</u> <u>flaws</u> which are not visible to the eye, e.g. cracks, reflect the ultrasounds. Computers analyse these reflections so that an assessment of the quality of the casting can be made.

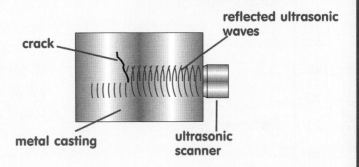

crack

reflected ultrasonic waves

metal casting

ultrasonic scanner

Examiner's Top Tip
To remember several uses of echoes and ultrasounds. Ultrasonic scanning of a foetus is a very important application that you should know.

- <u>Modern</u> <u>sonar</u> <u>equipment</u> uses ultrasounds. Ultrasonic waves can be emitted as a very narrow beam that does not spread out very much as it travels away from the source. Normal sound waves undergo <u>absorption</u> and spread out a lot as they travel through the water. The echoes these waves produce are weaker than those from the ultrasounds and therefore more difficult to detect.

QUICK TEST

1. What is an echo?
2. Give one use for echoes.
3. What is the hearing range of an average person?
4. What is an ultra sound?
5. Name three uses for ultrasounds.

5. Sonar, quality control, scanning unborn babies.
4. A sound that has a frequency which is too high for humans to hear.
3. 20 Hz – 20 000 Hz.
2. Echo sounding.
1. Reflection of a sound wave.

LOUDNESS AND THE DECIBEL SCALE

We measure loudness on the decibel scale.

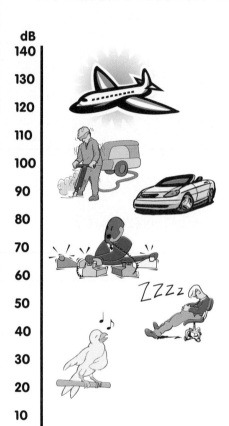

dB
140
130
120
110
100
90
80
70
60
50
40
30
20
10
0

- Constant exposure to loud sounds can damage your hearing.

- People who work with noisy machinery should wear ear defenders to protect their hearing.

- People listening to music through earphones should be careful not to have the volume turned up too high. The damage caused to their hearing by persistent exposure to loud sounds could be permanent.

Key Terms

Make sure you understand the following terms before moving on:
- Echo
- Sonar
- Hearing range
- Ultrasounds
- Loudness
- Decibel scale

SEISMIC WAVES

Seismic <u>waves</u> are <u>shock</u> <u>waves</u> caused by <u>earthquakes</u>. They travel through the Earth starting from the epicentre. Seismic waves can cause tremendous damage to buildings and structures on the Earth's surface. There are two main types of seismic waves. They are called <u>P-waves</u> (Primary waves) and <u>S-waves</u> (Secondary waves). Knowing the properties of P-waves and S-waves allows scientists to learn about the internal structure of the Earth.

INTERNAL STRUCTURE OF THE EARTH

The Earth is not a solid ball of rock, it has a layered structure.

· <u>The crust</u>: a thin outer layer.
· <u>The mantle</u>: a hot solid which has some liquid properties, i.e. it can flow, but extremely slowly like thick tar.
· <u>The outer core</u>: a very hot liquid made of molten iron and nickel.
· <u>The inner core</u>: a very hot solid.

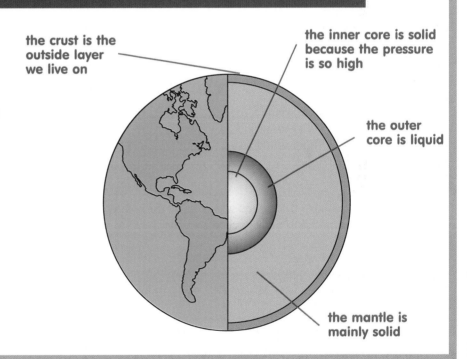

the crust is the outside layer we live on

the inner core is solid because the pressure is so high

the outer core is liquid

the mantle is mainly solid

- -

QUICK TEST

1. What on the decibel scale would be the reading for:
   a) complete silence
   b) normal conversation
   c) noisy machinery?
2. How can workers avoid damage to their hearing if they use noisy machinery in their work?
3. Name the four main parts of the structure of the Earth.

EXAM QUESTIONS —

1. What do waves carry from place to place?

....

2. Look at the diagram of a wave shown on the right. What is A? What is B?

....

3. Name three ways in which the direction of a wave can be changed.

....

4. Which reflected ray shows the direction of the incident ray
   after striking the mirror, A, B, C or D?

....

5. Explain why a flash of lightning is seen before the sound of thunder is heard.

....

6. Large objects vibrate slowly and produce.........pitched notes.

....

7. Sound waves can travel through solids, liquids and gases but not through a.........

....

8. A vibrating object produces 25 complete waves each second. What is the frequency of the sound it produces?

....

9. The diagrams (right) show wave patterns.
   Match each of the patterns with the descriptions
   A, B, C and D.
   i) A low pitched quiet sound...................
   ii) A high pitched loud sound...................
   iii) A low pitched loud sound...................
   iv) A high pitched quiet sound.................

10. a) What is an echo?   b) If sound waves travel through water at 1500 m/s how deep is the ocean below a ship
    which hears an echo from the seabed after just 1 s?   c) What would happen if a shoal of fish swam beneath
    the ship?

....

11. Which colour is refracted most when white light passes through a prism? What is the name of the band of
    colours produced by the prism?

....

12. What is Sonar?

....

13. What is a lens?

....

14. The diagram (below) shows a ray of light travelling through a glass block.
    Explain what happens to the ray of light as it enters the block.
    What would happen to the ray if it struck the surface at 90º?

....

15. A man stands 3 m in front of a plane mirror. Where is his image?

....

16. What is ultrasound? Give one use of ultrasound in hospitals.

....

17. The diagram (right) shows a ray of light striking the inside surface of a semi-circular glass block.

    a) What is the name of angle A? ....

    b) What happens to the ray if it strikes the surface at an angle

  i) smaller than angle A and ii) bigger than angle A?

....

18. a) Explain what happened to the ray of light when it struck the surface AB.

    b) Through what angle is the ray turned?

    c) Give one use for a prism which is used in this way.

....

19. Explain why a ray of light entering an optical fibre is unable to escape
    through the glass sides. Give one use for optical fibres.

....

20. What are 'ear defenders' and who should use them?

....

21. The diagram below shows the electromagnetic spectrum.

A	X-rays	Ultra-violet	Visible light	Infra-red	Microwaves	B

    a) Name the groups of waves A and B...

    b) Name three properties which are common to all members of the electromagnetic spectrum............

    c) Name two differences between the groups A and B...

    d) Name two groups that could be used for cooking..

    e) Name three groups that could be used for communicating...

    f) Name three groups that could cause cancer...

    g) Name one group used for seeing bones inside the body..

How did you do?

1–5	correct ....start again
6–11	correct ....getting there
12–16	correct ....good work
17–21	correct ....excellent

STATIC ELECTRICITY

Did you know that lightning is caused by static electricity?

WHERE DO ELECTRIC CHARGES COME FROM?

- *Atoms contain <u>positively</u> <u>charged</u> <u>particles</u> called <u>protons</u> within the nucleus.*
- *They also contain <u>negatively</u> <u>charged</u> <u>particles</u> called <u>electrons</u> which orbit the nucleus.*
- *<u>Neutral</u> <u>atoms</u> have <u>equal</u> <u>numbers</u> of protons and electrons.*

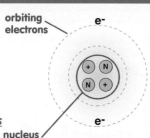

orbiting electrons

nucleus

a neutral atom

+ **positively charged proton**

N **uncharged particle (neutron)**

e⁻ **negatively charged electron**

HOW DO WE MAKE STATIC ELECTRICITY?

- Electrons belonging to one object can sometimes be <u>transferred</u> to another object simply by rubbing them together.
- Both objects should be <u>insulators</u>, i.e. made from plastic, cloth etc. Neither of them should be <u>conductors</u>, i.e. made from a metal.
- Insulators <u>do</u> <u>not</u> <u>allow</u> charges to pass through them.
- Conductors <u>allow</u> charges to pass through them easily.
- As the insulators are rubbed together one of them <u>gains</u> <u>electrons</u> and becomes <u>negatively</u> <u>charged</u>.
- The other <u>loses</u> <u>electrons</u> and becomes <u>positively</u> <u>charged</u>.

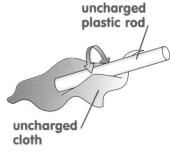

uncharged plastic rod

uncharged cloth

rod gains electrons and becomes negatively charged

cloth loses electrons and becomes positively charged

FORCES BETWEEN CHARGES

- Similar charges <u>repel</u>.
- If similar charges are given to each of the hairs on your head they will all repel each other. The result of these repulsions is that your hair will stand on end.
- Opposite charges <u>attract</u>.

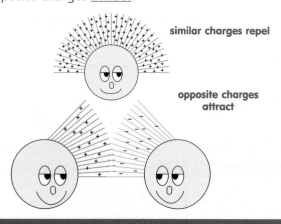

similar charges repel

opposite charges attract

INDUCED CHARGES

Even uncharged objects can be made to attract.

- Comb your hair with a plastic comb. This is likely to create some static electricity.
- Hold the comb close to some small pieces of paper. See how they are attracted to the comb.
- If the comb is <u>positively</u> <u>charged</u> it will <u>attract</u> <u>electrons</u> in the paper towards it.
- The far side of the paper will become <u>positively</u> <u>charged</u>.
- <u>Separating</u> <u>charges</u> likes this is called <u>charging</u> by <u>induction</u>.
- The <u>attractive</u> <u>force</u> is <u>greater</u> than the <u>repulsive</u> <u>force</u> because the opposite charges are <u>closer</u>.

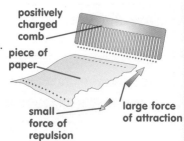

positively charged comb

piece of paper

small force of repulsion

large force of attraction

USES OF STATIC ELECTRICITY

ELECTROSTATIC SPRAYING

- **The nozzle of the spray is connected to the <u>positive terminal</u>.**

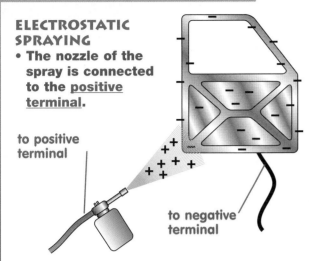

to positive terminal

to negative terminal

- **The paint droplets become <u>positively charged</u> as they emerge from the nozzle.**
- **<u>Repulsion</u> between the <u>similarly charged droplets</u> keeps the paint as a <u>fine spray</u>.**
- **The object to be painted is connected to a <u>negative</u> terminal.**
- **The paint is attracted to the <u>oppositely charged object</u>.**
- **Less paint is wasted and really awkward spots still get a good coat of paint.**

REMOVING DUST FROM SMOKE

- **As the dust particles (ash) pass through the first set of plates they become <u>positively charged</u>.**
- **As they pass through the second set they are <u>attracted by the opposite charge</u>.**
- **The ash sticks to the negative plates.**
- **The cleaner smoke continues up the chimney.**
- **Every so often the plates are shaken to remove the ash.**

smoke with dust removed

smoke and positively charged dust particles

negative −

positive +

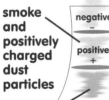

smoke and dust

VOLTAGE, SPARKS AND EARTHING

- As the amount of charge on an <u>isolated object</u> increases, the <u>repulsion</u> between charges and the <u>voltage</u> also increases.
- If the voltage becomes large enough the charges may jump gaps in order to escape (<u>discharging</u>).
- If this happens you may hear and see a spark, e.g. lightning.
- Sparking can be dangerous.
- Aeroplanes sometimes become <u>electrically charged</u> in <u>flight</u>.
- If a refuelling tanker approaches the plane on landing before the charges are removed a <u>discharging</u> <u>spark</u> <u>could</u> <u>cause</u> <u>an</u> <u>explosion</u>.
- The charge is removed safely by earthing the plane, i.e. a wire is attached to it to <u>provide</u> <u>an</u> <u>escape</u> <u>route</u> <u>for</u> <u>the</u> <u>charges</u>. Sometimes you can be the route to Earth!

QUICK TEST

1. What are the names of the charged particles of an atom?
2. How do the numbers of each type of charged particle compare in a neutral atom?
3. Which particles move when an object becomes charged?
4. Explain the difference between a conductor and an insulator.
5. Give one use of static electricity.
6. Give one disadvantage of static electricity.

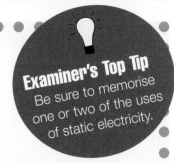

6. Danger of sparks and explosions.
5. Paint spraying.
4. Conductors allow charges to flow through them, insulators do not.
3. Electrons.
2. There are equal numbers of each.
1. Protons and electrons.

CURRENT, CHARGE AND ENERGY

MAKING CHARGES FLOW

Cells can be connected together to make a battery.

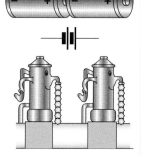

- _Cells_ and _batteries_ act as _charge pumps_, giving the charges _energy_.
- _Several cells connected together can give more energy to the charges and produce a larger current in the circuit._
- _Several cells connected together are called a _battery_._
- _Be sure to connect the cells so that they are all pumping in the same direction._

We can think of cells and batteries as charge pumps.

CHARGES ON THE MOVE

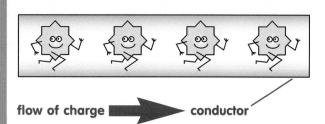

flow of charge ➡ conductor

insulator

I can't move through this!

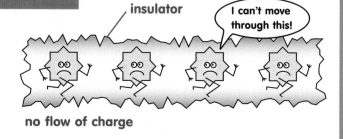

no flow of charge

- An electric current is a _flow of charge_.
- In _metals_ the charges are normally carried around by _electrons_.
- Metals are _good conductors_ because they contain lots of electrons that _are able to move around easily_.
- Non-metals are mainly _poor conductors or insulators_ because _they do not allow charges to move through them easily_.
- In conducting liquids the charges are carried by _charged particles_ called _ions_.

CURRENT PASSING THROUGH A LIQUID

Positive ions move towards negative electrode.

Negative ions move towards positive electrode.

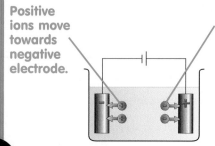

- **Many liquids contain <u>charged particles</u> called <u>ions</u>.**
- **When a voltage is applied across the liquid some of the positive ions move towards the <u>negative</u> terminal.**
- **Some of the <u>negative ions</u> move towards the <u>positive</u> terminal.**
- **This flow of charge is an <u>electric current</u>.**

MEASURING CURRENT

bulb

ammeter measuring the current flowing through the bulb

- We <u>measure</u> <u>current</u> with an <u>ammeter</u>.
- The size of a current is the <u>rate</u> <u>at</u> <u>which</u> <u>charge</u> <u>is</u> <u>flowing</u>.
- <u>Charge</u> (<u>Q</u>) is measured in <u>coulombs</u> (<u>C</u>).

- <u>Current</u> (<u>I</u>) is measured in <u>amps</u> <u>or</u> <u>amperes</u> (<u>A</u>).
- I = Q/t
- If a current of 3 A passes through the bulb, 3 C of charge flows through it each second.

GIVING ENERGY AWAY

- As charges flow around a circuit they <u>give</u> <u>away</u> <u>the</u> <u>energy</u> they gained from the cell or battery.
- This <u>energy</u> <u>is</u> <u>transferred</u> <u>into</u> <u>other</u> <u>forms</u> by the components in the circuit.
- A bulb <u>transfers</u> electrical energy into heat and light energy.
- A resistor <u>transfers</u> electrical energy into heat energy.
- A buzzer <u>transfers</u> electrical energy into sound energy.

HOW MUCH ENERGY IS TRANSFERRED?

- The <u>voltage</u> or <u>potential</u> <u>difference</u> (<u>pd</u>) tells us <u>how</u> <u>much</u> <u>energy</u> <u>is</u> <u>transferred</u> by a component in a circuit.
- A <u>pd</u> <u>of 1 V</u> means <u>1 J</u> <u>of</u> <u>electrical</u> <u>energy</u> <u>is</u> <u>being</u> <u>transferred</u> into other forms <u>every</u> <u>time</u> <u>1 C</u> <u>of</u> <u>charge</u> passes through a component.
- We measure the pd across a component using a <u>voltmeter</u>.
- This voltmeter (right) is measuring a pd of 4 V across the bulb.
- The bulb is changing <u>4 J</u> <u>of</u> <u>electrical</u> <u>energy</u> into <u>4 J</u> <u>of</u> <u>heat</u> <u>and</u> <u>light</u> <u>energy</u> every time <u>1 C</u> <u>of</u> <u>charge</u> <u>passes</u> <u>through</u> <u>the</u> <u>bulb</u>.

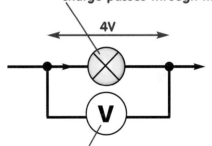

This bulb is changing 4 J of electrical energy into 4 J of heat and light energy every time 1 C of charge passes through it.

4V

Voltmeter, measuring the potential difference across the bulb.

QUICK TEST

1. **What is an electric current?**
2. **In what units do we measure a) charge, b) current, c) energy and d) pd?**
3. **What instrument do we use to measure a) current and b) pd?**
4. **What is a battery?**
5. **Explain why metals are good conductors of electricity and non-metals are mainly poor conductors**

5. Metals contain lots of 'free' electrons that can flow; non-metals do not.
4. Several cells connected together.
3. a) Ammeter, b) voltmeter.
2. a) Coulombs (C), b) amps or amperes (A), c) joules (J), d) volts (V).
1. A flow of charge.

CIRCUITS

- Currents pass around <u>complete</u> <u>circuits</u>.
- Current will not pass through a circuit if it is <u>incomplete</u>.
- There are two types of circuit: <u>series</u> <u>circuits</u> and <u>parallel</u> <u>circuits</u>.

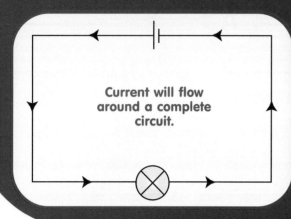

Current will flow around a complete circuit.

Current will not flow around a circuit if it is incomplete.

SERIES CIRCUITS

- Series circuits have no branches or junctions.
1. There is only one path for the current to follow.
2. They can be turned on and off by a single switch anywhere in the circuit: 'one out all out'.
3. The same current flows through all parts of the circuit.
4. The sum of the voltages across all the components is equal to the voltage across the cell or battery.

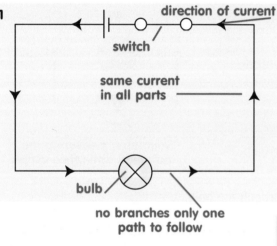

1

direction of current

switch

same current in all parts

bulb

no branches only one path to follow

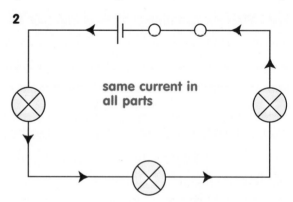

2

same current in all parts

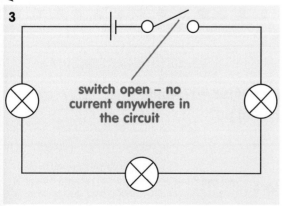

3

switch open – no current anywhere in the circuit

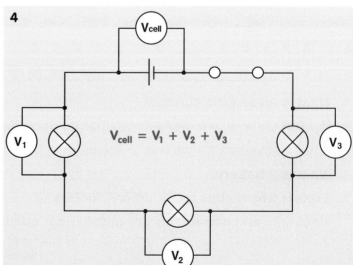

4

V_{cell}

V_1

$V_{cell} = V_1 + V_2 + V_3$

V_3

V_2

PARALLEL CIRCUITS

- Parallel circuits have branches and junctions.
- There is more than one path for the current to follow.
- Switches can be put into the circuit to turn on and off all or part of the circuit.
- The size of currents flowing in different parts of the circuit may be different.
- However, the current passing into a junction must be equal to the current passing out of the junction.
- The voltages across all branches of a parallel network are the same.

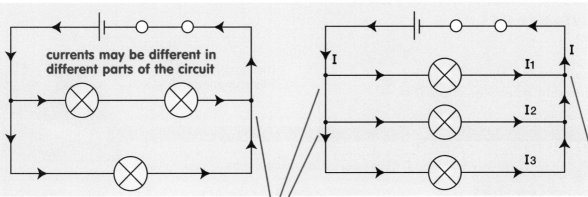

currents may be different in different parts of the circuit

circuits have branches and more than one path to follow

different currents, but currents passing into junction = currents passing out i.e. $I = I_1 + I_2 + I_3$

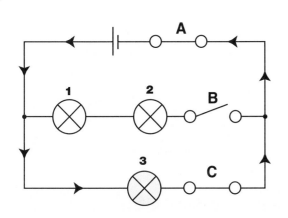

Opening switch B turns off bulbs 1 and 2, but current can still be in bulb 3. Bulb 3 can be turned on and off with switch C.
Switch A can turn all three bulbs on and off.

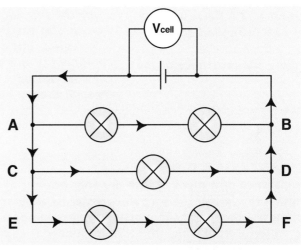

$$V_{cell} = V_{AB} = V_{CD} = V_{EF}$$

QUICK TEST

1. A circuit which has no gaps is called a .... circuit.

2. In which type of circuit:

   a) is the current the same everywhere?

   b) can just part of the circuit be turned off?

   c) are there branches or junctions?

3. If two currents of 2 A and 1 A pass into a junction, what size current passes out of the junction?

1. Complete.
2. a) series, b) parallel, c) parallel.
3. 3 A.

ELECTRICAL RESISTANCE

COMPONENTS IN A CIRCUIT **RESIST** CURRENT PASSING THROUGH THEM. THEY HAVE **RESISTANCE**. WE MEASURE THE RESISTANCE OF A COMPONENT IN **OHMS** (Ω). IF, WHEN A PD OF 1 V IS APPLIED ACROSS A COMPONENT, A CURRENT OF 1 A FLOWS: THE COMPONENT HAS A RESISTANCE OF 1 Ω.

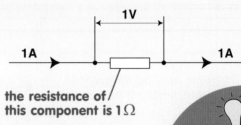

the resistance of this component is 1 Ω

We can express this relationship as an equation: $R = \dfrac{V}{I}$

Examiner's Top Tip
The equation $R = \dfrac{V}{I}$ is extremely important and is required on most exam papers.

EXAMPLE

EXAMPLE
A current of 3 A flows when a pd of 12 V is applied across wire.
Calculate the resistance of the wire.

$$R = \frac{V}{I} = \frac{12\,V}{3\,A} = 4\,\Omega$$

Using the formula triangle we can also use this equation to calculate pds across components and the currents passing through them.

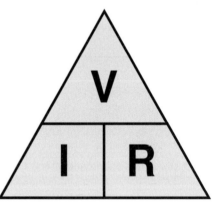

RESISTANCE OF A PIECE OF WIRE
The resistance of a piece of wire depends upon:
* length – the <u>longer</u> <u>the</u> <u>wire</u> the <u>greater</u> <u>its</u> <u>resistance</u>.
* thickness – the <u>larger</u> <u>the</u> <u>cross-sectional</u> <u>area</u> of a wire the <u>smaller</u> <u>its</u> <u>resistance</u>.
* the <u>material</u> from which the wire is made, e.g. copper wires have a low resistance and so are often used as connecting wires.

USING RESISTORS

We can use <u>resistors</u> to control the <u>size</u> <u>of</u> <u>the</u> <u>current</u> in a circuit.
If a <u>variable</u> <u>resistor</u> is included in a circuit its value can be altered so that the current around a circuit can be changed easily.

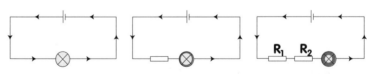

With no resistors in the circuit, a large current will flow.

With a resistor in the circuit, a smaller current will flow.

When several resistors are connected in series in the circuit an even smaller current flows. The total resistance of the resistors = $R_1 + R_2$ where R_1 and R_2 are resistance values of components.

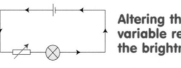

Altering the value of this variable resistor changes the brightness of the bulb.

SPECIAL RESISTORS

LIGHT-DEPENDENT RESISTORS (LDRs)

- These have a <u>high</u> <u>resistance</u> when there is <u>little</u> <u>or</u> <u>no light</u>.
- Their <u>resistance decreases</u> as <u>light intensity increases</u>.
- They are used in <u>light-sensitive circuits</u>, e.g. for controlling <u>street lighting</u> or in <u>burglar alarms</u>.

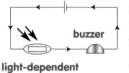

simple burglar alarm

If the burglar turns on the light the resistance of the LDR falls. Current now flows around the circuit and the buzzer sounds.

light-dependent resistor (LDR)

THERMISTORS

- These are resistors whose <u>resistance alters</u> greatly as their <u>temperature changes</u>.
- Unlike wires the vast majority of these resistors have <u>resistances that decrease</u> as their <u>temperature increases</u>.
- They are used in <u>temperature-sensitive circuits</u>, e.g. <u>fire alarms</u> <u>and thermostats</u>.

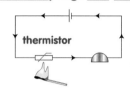

simple fire alarm

As the thermistor becomes warm its resistance falls. Current now flows around the circuit and the buzzer sounds.

OHM'S LAW

- If a range of pds is applied across a piece of wire and the currents that pass through it are measured, a <u>current–voltage graph</u> can be drawn for the wire.
- Providing the temperature of the wire does not change, the graph will be a <u>straight line passing through the origin</u>.
- This shape of graph shows that the <u>current</u> passing through the wire is <u>directly proportional to the pd</u> across its ends, providing its temperature does not alter.
- This conclusion is known as <u>Ohm's Law</u>.
- Components that obey this law are called <u>ohmic-conductors</u>.

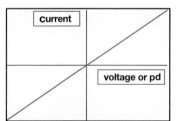

I–V graph for a length of wire. The steeper the line the lower the resistance.

- The current–voltage graph for a filament bulb is <u>not a</u> <u>straight line</u> passing through the origin.

- As the current passing through it increases its temperature increases and so too does its resistance.

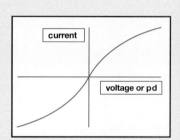

- The current–voltage graph for a diode is not a straight line.

- The resistance of a diode is low in one direction but high in the opposite direction.

- <u>Diodes</u> are used in circuits to ensure that current only flows in <u>one</u> <u>direction</u>.

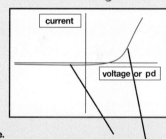

I–V graph for a diode.
The resistance of the diode in this direction is high.
The resistance of the diode is very low. —
Remember – the steeper the graph the lower the resistance.

QUICK TEST

1. In what units do we measure resistance?
2. Name three features of a piece of wire which affect its resistance.
3. Calculate the resistance of a fixed resistor which has a current of 2 A flowing through it when a pd of 9 V is applied across its ends.
4. What type of component is affected by the intensity of light? Give one use for this type of component.
5. What type of component decreases its resistance as its temperature increases? Give one use for this type of component.
6. What is the total resistance when 2 Ω, 3 Ω and 5 Ω resistors are connected in series?

6. 10 Ω.
5. Thermistor; fire alarm.
4. Light-dependent resistor (LDR); control street lights.
3. 4.5 Ω.
2. Length, thickness, material.
1. Ohms (Ω).

ELECTRICAL POWER

- All <u>electrical</u> <u>appliances</u> change <u>electrical</u> <u>energy</u> in to <u>other forms</u> <u>of</u> <u>energy</u>.
- A hair drier changes <u>electrical</u> <u>energy</u> into <u>heat</u>, <u>kinetic</u> and some <u>sound</u> <u>energy</u>.
- A radio changes <u>electrical</u> <u>energy</u> into <u>sound</u> <u>energy</u>.
- The power of an appliance is a measure of how <u>quickly</u> these energy changes take place. This <u>power</u> <u>rating</u> is measured in <u>watts</u>.

THE MEANING OF POWER

If a light bulb has a <u>power</u> <u>rating</u> of 40 W, it changes 40 J of electrical energy into heat and light energy every second.

If an electrical fire has a <u>power</u> <u>rating of</u> <u>2 kW</u> (2000 W), it changes 2000 J of <u>electrical</u> <u>energy</u> into 2000 J of heat and light energy <u>every</u> <u>second</u>.

HOW MANY JOULES OF ENERGY HAVE BEEN CONVERTED?

To calculate the total amount of energy an appliance has converted we use the equation:

in watts   in seconds

$$\text{Energy} = \text{Power} \times \text{time} \qquad \text{or } E = P \times t$$

EXAMPLE

How much electrical energy is converted into heat and light energy when a 60 W bulb is turned on for five minutes?

$E = P \times t = 60 \times 300 = 18000$ J or 18 kJ

KILOWATT-HOURS AND UNITS

An electricity supplier measures the energy we use in the home in <u>kilowatt-hours (kWh)</u>, or <u>units</u>.

They calculate this value using the formula:

Energy used in kilowatt-hours = Power in kilowatts x time in hours

EXAMPLE

Calculate the energy used when a 3 kW fire is turned on for two hours.

$E = P \times t = 3$ kW x 2 h = 6 kWh or 6 units

Examiner's Top Tip
Draw out the equation E = P x t as a formula triangle, then try doing some problems where you have to find the values of P or t.

THE METER AND THE BILL

- Somewhere in your house is a <u>meter</u> like the one pictured. It shows how many <u>units of electrical energy</u> have been used.

- We usually pay our electricity bills every three months, i.e. every quarter.

- By reading the meter at the beginning and end of the quarter we can calculate how many units of electrical energy have been used.

ELECTRICITY BILL				
Charges for electricity used				
Present reading 80139	**Previous reading** 78579	**Units used** 1560	**Pence per unit** 6.00	**Charge amount** £93.60
Quarterly standing charge				£13.00
Total				£106.60

- The bill shows the <u>number of units used</u> and <u>the cost per unit</u>.

- By multiplying these two values together we can obtain the cost of the electrical energy used.

- The electricity board will also add to your bill a <u>standing charge</u>. This pays for the equipment used by the electricity board in bringing the electricity into your home and its maintenance.

EXAMPLE

The readings on an electricity meter at the beginning and end of a quarter show that a family has used 800 units. If the cost of one unit is 11p and the standing charge per quarter is £12. Calculate the total bill for this household.

Cost of electricity = number of units used x cost per unit =

    800 x 11p = £88.00

If the standing charge is £12 the total cost of the bill is £88.00 + £12 = £100

QUICK TEST

1. How many joules of electrical energy are used in the following situations:

   a) 100 W bulb turned on for one minute?

   b) 500 W computer and monitor turned on for five minutes?

   c) 600 W hair drier turned on for two minutes?

   d) 1000 W heater turned on for four minutes?

   e) 2 kW tumble drier turned on for five minutes?

2. How many units of electricity are used in the following situations:

   a) 3 kW fire turned on for three hours?

   b) 2 kW tumble drier used for 30 minutes?

   c) 1.5 kW water heater turned on for two hours?

   d) 500 W TV turned on for four hours?

   e) 100 W radio turned on for 10 hours?

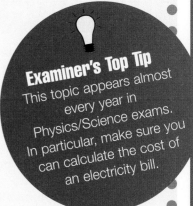

2. a) 9 units,   b) 1 unit,   c) 3 units,   d) 2 units,   e) 1 unit.

1. a) 6000 J,   b) 150000 J,   c) 72000 J,   d) 240000 J,   e) 600000 J.

DOMESTIC ELECTRICITY

- The electricity we use in the home is known as <u>mains</u> <u>electricity</u>.
- It is generated at a power station and then transmitted to us through the National Grid.
- It differs from the electricity we use from cells and batteries in several ways.

A.C./D.C.

- *The electricity we get from cells and batteries is <u>one-way</u> <u>electricity</u>.*
- *It is called <u>direct</u> <u>current</u> (<u>d.c.</u>).*
- *The electricity from the mains is <u>continuously</u> <u>changing</u> <u>direction</u>.*
- *It is <u>alternating</u> <u>current</u> (<u>a.c.</u>).*
- *It passes back and forth <u>50</u> <u>times</u> <u>every</u> <u>second</u>, i.e. it has a <u>frequency</u> <u>of</u> <u>50</u> <u>Hz</u>.*

An instrument called the Cathode Ray Oscilloscope

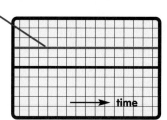

Horizontal line shows current/ voltage has a steady value and passes in one direction. This is a d.c. current from a cell or battery.

The electricity we get from the mains.

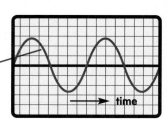

'Wave-shaped' line shows an a.c. current/voltage which is continually changing direction.

THE THREE-PIN PLUG

- The voltage of the electricity from cells and batteries is quite low, e.g. 9 V, 12 V.
- The voltage from the mains is about 230 V, which can kill a person.
- It <u>can</u> <u>be</u> <u>dangerous</u> if not used safely.
- Most appliances are therefore connected to the mains using <u>insulated</u> <u>plugs</u>.
- It is very important that the wires in a plug are connected to the <u>correct</u> <u>pins</u>.
- Looking at an open plug like the one shown here the <u>BR</u>own wire goes to the <u>B</u>ottom <u>R</u>ight and the <u>BL</u>ue wire goes to the <u>B</u>ottom <u>L</u>eft. The blue and yellow wire goes to the pin at the top.

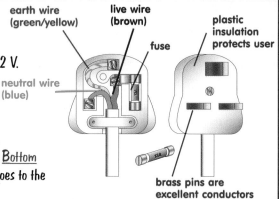

earth wire (green/yellow)   live wire (brown)   plastic insulation protects user   fuse   neutral wire (blue)   brass pins are excellent conductors

THE EARTH WIRE

- A three-pin plug usually has three wires connected to it.
- The <u>electrical</u> <u>energy</u> travels into an appliance through the <u>live</u> <u>wire</u>.
- The <u>neutral</u> <u>wire</u> is the <u>return</u> <u>path</u> for the current.
- The <u>earth</u> <u>wire</u> is a safety connection which <u>protects</u> <u>the</u> <u>user</u> if an appliance becomes faulty.
- If the kettle has a metal casing and the heating element is broken, anyone touching the casing of the kettle will receive an electric shock.
- With the <u>earth</u> <u>wire</u> <u>connected</u> the user is safe and will not receive an electric shock.
- Modern appliances such as kettles now have <u>plastic</u> <u>casings</u> to reduce the further risk of an electric shock for the user.
- The kettle has <u>double</u> <u>insulation</u>.

Replacing the metal with a plastic casing gives the user double insulation.

FUSES

- All three-pin UK plugs contain a <u>fuse</u>.
- This usually consists of a small <u>cylinder</u> <u>or</u> <u>cartridge</u> containing a thin piece of <u>wire</u> with a <u>low</u> <u>melting</u> <u>point</u>.
- If a fault develops in a circuit and <u>too</u> <u>much</u> <u>current</u> passes through the fuse, the <u>wire</u> <u>melts</u>.
- The circuit becomes <u>incomplete</u> and current ceases to pass through it.
- The fuse <u>protects</u> <u>the</u> <u>user</u> and <u>limits</u> <u>any</u> <u>damage</u> to the electrical appliance.

- Fuses are given a <u>rating</u> which indicates the <u>maximum</u> <u>current</u> that can pass through it without it melting.
- The most common fuses in the UK have ratings of <u>1 A</u>, <u>3 A</u>, <u>5 A</u> and <u>13 A</u>.

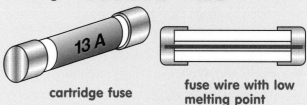

cartridge fuse   **fuse wire with low melting point**

WHICH FUSE?

- **Choosing the correct value of fuse for a circuit is important.**
- **If the fuse selected has too low a rating it will melt (blow) and turn off the circuit even when there is no fault and the correct current is passing through.**
- **If the fuse has too high a rating it will not protect the circuit when too large a current passes through.**
- **The correct value of a fuse is one which is <u>just</u> <u>large</u> <u>enough</u> <u>to</u> <u>allow</u> <u>the</u> <u>correct</u> <u>current</u> <u>to</u> <u>pass</u> <u>through</u>, e.g. if the normal current is 2 A then a 3 A fuse is selected.**

CIRCUIT BREAKERS

These are a <u>special</u> <u>kind</u> <u>of</u> <u>fuse</u> which cause a break in a circuit if too much current passes through. Once the fault has been put right the fuse is usually <u>reset</u> by pushing a button.

CALCULATING THE CORRECT VALUE

If we know the <u>power</u> <u>rating</u> of an appliance connected to the mains supply we can calculate the correct fuse that should be used in this circuit using the equation:

$$I = \frac{P}{V}$$

EXAMPLE

Calculate the correct fuse needed for a fire rated at 240 V 3 kW.

$$I = \frac{P}{V} = \frac{3\,000}{240} = 12.5 \text{ A}$$

The correct fuse to use would therefore be a 13 A fuse.

EXAMPLE

Calculate the correct fuse needed for a hair drier rated at 230 V 1000 W.

$$I = \frac{P}{V} = \frac{1000}{230} = 4.3 \text{ A}$$

The correct fuse in this case would be a 5 A fuse.

QUICK TEST

1. What kind of current is supplied through the mains?

2. Why can the mains supply be dangerous?

3. In a typical domestic plug what colour is:

   a) the live wire?

   b) the earth wire?

   c) the neutral wire?

4. Why are the pins of the domestic plug made from brass?

5. What happens to a cylinder fuse if too much current passes through it?

6. Name one advantage of a circuit breaker over a cylinder fuse.

7. What is the casing of a doubly insulated appliance likely to be made from?

7. Plastic.
6. It can be reset.
5. The wire melts.
4. Brass is a very good conductor of electricity.
3. a) brown b) green and yellow c) blue
2. It is of high voltage (230 V).
1. AC (alternating current).

MAGNETISM AND ELECTROMAGNETISM

MAGNETS

- **Magnets** attract **magnetic materials**, e.g. iron, steel, nickel and cobalt.
- **Magnets** do not attract **non-magnetic materials**, e.g. wood, plastic, copper, aluminium.

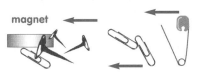

magnetic materials e.g. iron, steel, nickel, cobalt

non-magnetic materials e.g. plastic, paper, wood

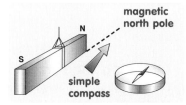

magnetic north pole

simple compass

- The **strongest parts** of a magnet are its **poles**.
- All magnets have **two poles**: a **north pole** and a **south pole**.
- A bar magnet suspended horizontally will align itself with the Earth's magnetic field so that its north pole points towards geographical north and its south pole points towards geographical south. The magnet behaves like **a compass**.

similar poles repel

| N | N |

| S | N |

opposite poles attract

MAGNETIC FIELDS

- The space around a magnet is occupied by a **magnetic field**. In this space, magnetic attraction and repulsion can be **detected**.
- The shape of the magnetic field around a bar magnet can be seen using iron filings or plotting compasses.

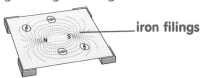

iron filings

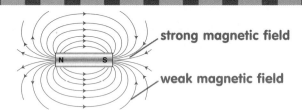

strong magnetic field

weak magnetic field

- The **shape**, strength and direction of magnetic fields is shown using **magnetic field lines**.
- The lines are **close together** where the field is **strong**.
- The lines are **far apart** where the field is **weak**.
- The direction of the field is from **north to south**.

ELECTROMAGNETISM

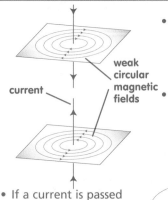

weak circular magnetic fields

current

- If a current is passed through a wire, a weak circular magnetic field is created around the wire.

- If the direction of the current in the wire is changed, the direction of the magnetic field also changes.
- The Right Hand Thumb Rule can be used to determine the field direction.

current

field

Point the thumb of your right hand in the direction of the current and your finger will curl in the direction of the magnetic field.

- To make the magnetic field stronger we can increase the current or make the wire into a coil.

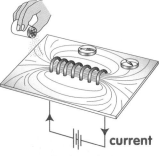

current

- A **long coil is called a solenoid**.
- The magnetic field around a coil or solenoid is the **same shape** as that of a bar magnet.
- The positions of the poles for a solenoid can be found using the **Right Hand Grip Rule**.

Wrap your finger in the direction of the current in the coils and your thumb will point to the north pole of the solenoid.

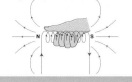

ELECTROMAGNETS

If a solenoid (a long coil) is wrapped on to a <u>core</u> made from a material such as <u>iron</u>, the strength of its magnetic field increases. This <u>combination</u> of <u>coil</u> and <u>core</u> is called an <u>electromagnet</u>. One of the main advantages of an electromagnet over a permanent magnet is that it can be turned on and off.

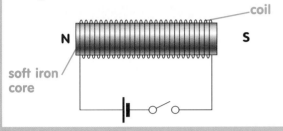

MAGNETICALLY HARD AND MAGNETICALLY SOFT MATERIALS

- Iron is a <u>magnetically</u> <u>soft</u> <u>material</u>.
- A magnetically soft material is <u>easy to</u> <u>magnetise</u> and <u>easily loses its magnetism</u>.
- A <u>magnetically</u> <u>hard material</u> is a little <u>difficult to</u> <u>magnetise</u> but once it is magnetised it <u>holds on to its</u> <u>magnetism</u>. Steel is a magnetically hard material. Some permanent magnets are made from steel.

USES OF ELECTROMAGNETS

ELECTRIC BELL

- When the bell push is pressed the circuit is complete and the electromagnet is turned on.
- The <u>soft iron armature</u> is pulled towards the electromagnet and the <u>hammer</u> hits the <u>gong</u>.
- At the same time a gap is created at C and the electromagnet is turned off.
- The armature now springs back to its original position and the whole process starts again.
- As long as the bell push is pressed, the armature will vibrate back and forth striking the gong.

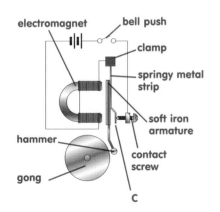

SCRAP-YARD ELECTROMAGNET

The soft iron core of this electromagnet is magnetised when the current is turned on but loses its magnetism when the current it is turned off.

- When current passes through the coil, a very strong electromagnet is created which is able to pick up cars.
- When the magnet is <u>turned off</u> the <u>magnetic</u> <u>field</u> <u>collapses</u> and the car is <u>released</u>.

RELAY SWITCH

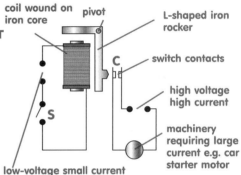

- This is a safety device. It is often used to <u>turn on a circuit</u> through which a <u>large (potentially dangerous) current</u> passes using a circuit through which a <u>small current passes</u>.
- When the switch S is closed, a small current flows, turning the electromagnet on.
- The <u>rocker</u> is pulled down and at the same time <u>the contacts at C</u> are pushed together.
- A large current now passes through the second circuit.
- When S is opened the <u>electromagnet is turned off</u>.
- The <u>rocker is released</u> and returns to its original position.
- The <u>contacts at C open</u> and <u>current ceases to pass through</u> the second circuit.

QUICK TEST

1. Name one magnetic material.
2. Name one non-magnetic material.
3. Why is steel used for making permanent magnets?
4. Why is iron used for the core of an electromagnet?
5. What is a solenoid?

5. Long coil.
4. It is magnetically soft and loses its magnetism when the current is turned off.
3. It is magnetically hard and keeps its magnetism.
2. Plastic.
1. Iron.

THE ELECTRIC MOTOR

FORCE ON A CURRENT-CARRYING WIRE

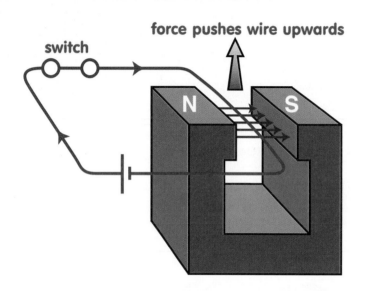

force pushes wire upwards

switch

N S

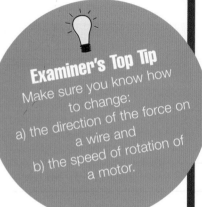

Examiner's Top Tip
Make sure you know how to change:
a) the direction of the force on a wire and
b) the speed of rotation of a motor.

- **If a current is passed through a <u>wire</u> which lies <u>between the poles</u> of a magnet, there is a <u>force</u> on the wire.**

- **If the <u>direction</u> of the <u>current</u> or the direction of the <u>magnetic field</u> is changed, the <u>direction of the force</u> on the wire <u>also changes</u>.**

THE ROTATING LOOP OF WIRE

- *If the length of wire is replaced by a <u>loop</u> of wire, when current passes around it, there will be a force on one side of the loop trying to push it <u>upwards</u>.*
- *There will also be a force on the <u>opposite</u> side of the loop trying to push it <u>downwards</u>.*
- *The effect of these two forces is to make the loop <u>rotate</u>.*
- *This is the basic idea behind the <u>electric motor</u>.*

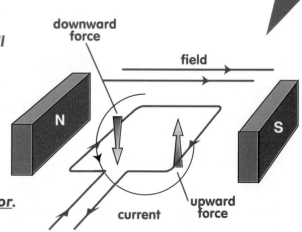

downward force

field

N

S

current

upward force

THE SIMPLE ELECTRIC MOTOR

- For the loop to <u>rotate</u> <u>continuously</u>, the direction of the <u>force</u> on each side must <u>change</u> <u>every</u> <u>half</u> <u>turn</u>, i.e. first a wire must be pushed up, then it must be pushed down.
- This change is achieved using a <u>split</u> <u>ring</u> or <u>commutator</u>.
- The split ring <u>changes</u> <u>the</u> <u>direction</u> of the current in the coil after <u>every</u> <u>half</u> <u>turn</u>.

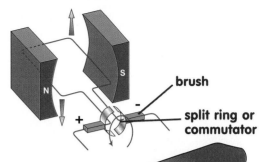

brush

split ring or commutator

TO MAKE A MOTOR TURN MORE QUICKLY
- Increase the <u>current</u>.
- Increase the <u>number</u> <u>of</u> <u>turns</u>.
- Increase the <u>strength</u> of the magnet.

REAL MOTORS
- In real, practical motors, the coils of wire are wrapped on to a <u>soft</u> <u>iron</u> <u>core</u>, which rotates with the coil. This makes the motor <u>more</u> <u>powerful</u>.
- <u>Several</u> <u>coils</u> wrapped on the same axis replace the single coil. This makes the motor <u>smoother</u> <u>and</u> <u>more</u> <u>powerful</u>.
- The permanent magnet is replaced with <u>electromagnets</u>.

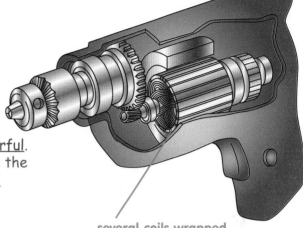

several coils wrapped on soft iron core electromagnets

THE MOVING COIL LOUDSPEAKER
- <u>Alternating</u> <u>currents</u> (currents that keep changing size and direction) from a radio or CD player are <u>passed</u> <u>through</u> <u>a</u> <u>coil</u> placed between the poles of a magnet.
- The coil will experience <u>forces</u> pushing it <u>back</u> <u>and</u> <u>forth</u>.
- A <u>paper</u> <u>cone</u> is attached to the coil.
- The movements of the coil <u>cause</u> <u>the</u> <u>cone</u> <u>to</u> <u>vibrate</u> creating <u>sound</u> <u>waves</u> in the air.

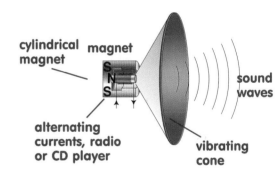

cylindrical magnet

magnet

sound waves

alternating currents, radio or CD player

vibrating cone

QUICK TEST

1. A wire lying between the poles of a magnet moves upwards when current is passed through it. What will happen to the wire if each of the following is altered?

   a) The direction of the current.

   b) The direction of the magnetic field.

   c) The direction of the current and the magnetic field.

2. What device changes the direction of the current in an electric motor every half turn?

3. State three ways of increasing the rate of rotation of an electric motor.

4. Why are several coils used in practical motors rather than just one?

5. What happens to a loudspeaker when alternating currents are passed through its coil?

5. The cone is moved backwards and forwards quickly, i.e. it is made to vibrate.
4. Smoother turning and more powerful.
3. Increase the current in the coil, increase the number of turns on the coil and increase the field strength of the magnets.
2. Split ring/commutator.
1. a) Wire moves down,   b) wire moves down,   c) wire moves up.

INDUCING A CURRENT/VOLTAGE INTO A WIRE

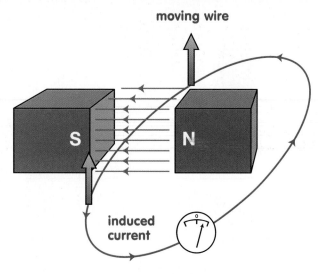

moving wire

induced current

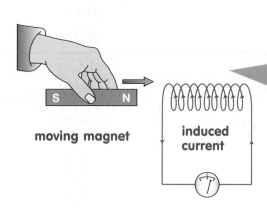

moving magnet

induced current

- If a wire is moved across a magnetic field as shown in the diagram above, a voltage is induced across the wire.
- If the wire is part of a **circuit**, a **current will flow**.
- If the wire is moved in the **opposite direction**, the **induced voltage** and **current** are in the opposite direction.
- If the wire is held **stationary no current** or **voltage** is induced.
- To increase the size of the voltage or current we could.
  a) use a **stronger magnet**.
  b) move the wire **more quickly**.

- If a **magnet is moved into a coil**, a **voltage or current is induced** in the coil.
- If the **magnet is pulled out**, the induced voltage or current is in **the opposite direction**.
- To **increase the size** of the induced voltage or current, we can:
  a) use a **stronger magnet**,
  b) **move the magnet faster**, or
  c) put **more turns on the coil**.

Currents and voltages can be created when magnetic field lines are cut by a conductor, e.g. a piece of wire. Producing currents and voltages in this way is called electromagnetic induction.

THE SIMPLE DYNAMO

A dynamo like that used on a bicycle is used to generate small currents.
- As the wheel rotates it turns the knurled knob.
- The magnet and its magnetic field spin around.
- Its magnetic field lines cut through the coil inducing a current in it.
- The current generated keeps changing size and direction.
- It is called an alternating current.

- This current can be used to work the bicycle's lights.
- If the cyclist stops, the wheel stops. There is no movement of the magnet and its field so there is no induced current and the lights will go out.

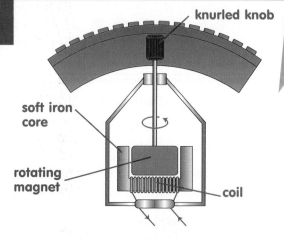

knurled knob

soft iron core

rotating magnet

coil

CRO shows the current/voltage generated by a dynamo.

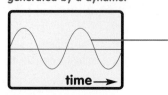

time →

The display shows a dynamo produces an alternating current/voltage.

ELECTROMAGNETIC INDUCTION

GENERATORS AND ALTERNATORS

- *If a <u>coil</u> is <u>rotated</u> between the poles of a magnet a <u>current</u> is <u>induced</u> in the coil.*
- *Because the wires are continually <u>changing direction</u> as they rotate, the induced current also changes size and direction.*
- *The induced current is an <u>alternating current</u>.*
- *A <u>generator</u> which produces alternating current is called an <u>alternator</u>.*
- *The coil will generate a larger current if a) a <u>stronger magnet</u> is used, b) the coil is <u>turned more quickly</u> or c) a coil with <u>more turns</u> is used.*

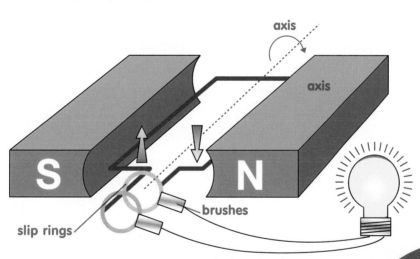

axis

axis

S   N

slip rings

brushes

induced voltage/current

Examiner's Top Tip
Don't let phrases like 'electromagnetic induction' and 'induced current' confuse you, just try to understand how voltages and currents can be made using magnetic fields and wires.

QUICK TEST

1. What will happen to the current induced in a wire if:

   a) the wire is moved more quickly through the field?

   b) the wire is held stationary in the field?

   c) the wire is moved parallel to the field?

   d) the wire is moved at the same speed but in the opposite direction?

2. What kind of current is produced when a magnet is rotated inside a coil?

3. Suggest two ways in which an alternator can be changed to produce a higher current.

3. Increase the speed of rotation; increase the strength of the magnetic field; increase the number of turns on the alternator's coil.

2. Alternating current.

1. a) Larger current,   b) no current,   c) no current,   d) same size current as a) but in opposite direction.

TRANSFORMERS

Transformers are used to change voltages; but only alternating voltages.
A transformer consists of two coils wrapped around a soft iron core.

HOW A TRANSFORMER WORKS

soft iron core linking the two coils

- An <u>alternating</u> <u>voltage</u> is applied across coil A, called the <u>primary</u> <u>coil</u>.
- It produces a magnetic field that is continuously changing.
- This changing magnetic field cuts through the coils of the secondary coil (B).
- An alternating voltage is induced across the secondary coil.

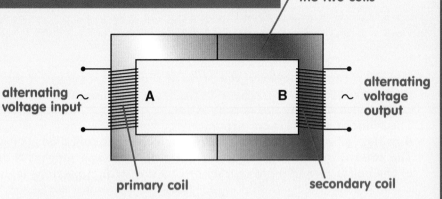

alternating voltage input

A   B

alternating voltage output

primary coil   secondary coil

HOW LARGE IS THE INDUCED VOLTAGE?

The size of the voltage (V_s) induced in the secondary coil depends upon the size of the voltage across the primary coil (V_p), the number of turns on the primary coil (N_p) and the number of turns on the secondary coil (N_s). They are linked by the equation:

$$\frac{V_s}{V_p} = \frac{N_s}{N_p}$$

EXAMPLE
Calculate the voltage across a secondary coil of a transformer if an alternating voltage of 12 V is applied across the coils of the primary.
The number of turns on the primary coil is 100 and the number of turns on the secondary coil is 500.

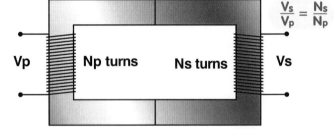

$$\frac{V_s}{V_p} = \frac{N_s}{N_p}$$

Vp   Np turns   Ns turns   Vs

Using $\dfrac{V_s}{V_p} = \dfrac{N_s}{N_p}$

$$V_s = \frac{N_s \times V_p}{N_p}$$

$$V_s = \frac{500 \times 12}{100}$$

$$V_s = 60\,V$$

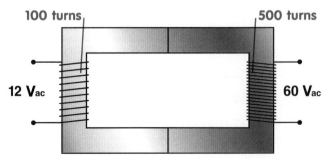

100 turns   500 turns

12 V$_{ac}$ 60 V$_{ac}$

A transformer like this which is used to increase voltages is called a <u>**step-up**</u> <u>**transformer**</u>.
If the transformer decreases voltages it is called a <u>**step-down**</u> <u>**transformer**</u>.

EFFICIENCY OF A TRANSFORMER

Transformers are very efficient. Most of the energy that enters the primary coils leaves through the secondary coil as useful energy. To make a transformer as efficient as possible:

- the turns of both coils are made from thick copper wires. This reduces any heat loss when current flows in the wires.
- the coils are linked by a soft iron core. This concentrates the field around the two coils.
- the iron core is <u>laminated</u>, i.e. it is made from <u>thin</u> <u>sheets</u> electrically insulated from their neighbours. This design stops large currents being created within the core by the moving magnetic field.

THE NATIONAL GRID

- Large alternators at power stations generate the electricity we use in our homes and factories.
- The electricity is transmitted along a <u>network</u> of cables and wires.
- As the electrical energy travels through the cables some of it is <u>wasted</u>. It is changed into <u>heat</u> and <u>warms</u> the cables.
- If the electrical energy is transmitted with a <u>high voltage</u> and a <u>small current</u>, this loss is <u>small</u>.
- A <u>step-up transformer</u> is used to achieve this change.
- This very high-voltage electricity is <u>dangerous</u>, so after transmission, before being supplied to factories and houses, the voltage is decreased by a <u>step-down transformer</u>.

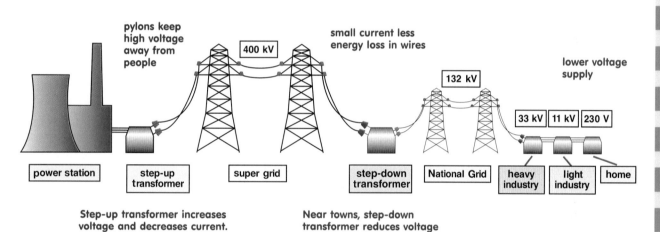

Step-up transformer increases voltage and decreases current.

Near towns, step-down transformer reduces voltage to safer levels.

QUICK TEST

1. What kind of voltages and currents can a transformer change?

2. What kind of a transformer:

   a) increases voltages?

   b) decreases voltages?

3. Name three ways in which the construction of a transformer makes it efficient.

4. Calculate the voltage across the secondary coil of the transformer if an alternating voltage of 20 V is applied across the coils of the primary. The number of turns on the primary coil is 400 and the number of turns on the secondary coil is 100.

5. Why is electrical energy transmitted through the National Grid at very high voltages and low currents?

6. Why is the voltage of the electrical supply decreased for supplies to houses?

1. Alternating (ac).
2. a) step-up, b) step-down.
3. Thick wire for coils, linking by soft iron core, laminated core.
4. 5 V.
5. To reduce energy loss.
6. Low voltage is safer.

EXAM QUESTIONS — Use the questions to test your progress. Check your answers on page 95.

1. What happens if two similarly charged objects are placed next to each other?

....

2. What happens if the north pole of one magnet is placed next to the south pole of another magnet?

....

3. Name the three particles that are contained in an atom. Which of these particles moves when current passes through a wire?

....

4. Why is it not possible to pick up pieces of paper using a magnet?

....

5. Give two uses for static electricity.

....

6. Name one magnetically soft and one magnetically hard material. Suggest one use for each.

....

7. What happens to a bar magnet if it is suspended horizontally in the Earth's magnetic field?

....

8. Give one advantage that electromagnets have over permanent magnets.

....

9. a) Why will charge flow in circuit A but not in circuit B?
   b) Explain how circuit B could be used to test materials to see if they are conductors or insulators.

....

10. To which part of an electrical appliance should the earth wire be connected?

....

11. What kind of electrical circuit contains different paths for the current to follow?

....

12. What device has a low resistance when charge passes in one direction but has a high resistance in the reverse direction?

....

13. What is a light-dependent resistor? Name one use for a light-dependent resistor.

....

14. State three ways in which the speed of rotation of a motor could be increased. What is the purpose of the split ring in an electric motor?

....

15. A current is induced in a coil as it rotates between the poles of a magnet. State three ways in which the size of the induced current could be increased.

....

....

16. What is the voltage across bulb A in the circuit?

....

....

....

17. Calculate the electrical energy used in units when a 2 kW fire is turned on for three hours. Calculate the cost of this energy if the cost of one unit is 11 pence.

....

18. Explain the difference between a direct current (d.c.) and an alternating current (a.c.).

....

19. Why is the electricity we use in the home transmitted across the country as a.c. at a high voltage and low current?

....

20. Calculate the power of a hair drier which, when connected to a 240 V supply, has a current of 5A flowing through it.

....

21. Calculate the resistance of a piece of wire which, when a pd of 6 V is applied across its ends, allows a current of 0.25 A to pass through it.

0.25 A

6 V

....

22. When a 3 kW fire is connected to an a.c. supply a current of 12.5 A flows. Calculate the voltage of the a.c. supply.

....

23. Calculate the correct fuse that should be included in a three-pin plug for a 1000 W 240 V hair drier.

....

24. A pd of 4 Vac is applied across the primary coil of a transformer. If the primary coil has 1000 turns and the secondary coil has 5000 turns and assuming that the transformer is 100% efficient:
    a) what is the pd produced by the transformer across its secondary coil?

....

    b) what kind of transformer is this?

....

How did you do?

1–6	correct	start again
7–12	correct	getting there
13–18	correct	good work
19–24	correct	excellent

KINETIC THEORY

The **kinetic theory** is a model which tries to explain the **properties of solids, liquids and gases**, using the **movement of particles**.

SOLIDS

- Particles in a **solid** have **fixed positions**.
- They are **close together**.
- If they are positioned in a **regular structure** they may form **crystals**.
- The **forces** holding them in position are **strong**, so solids have their own shape.

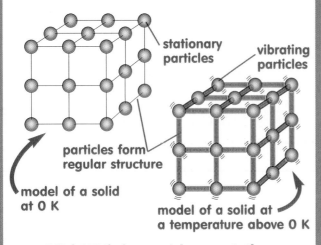

stationary particles

vibrating particles

particles form regular structure

model of a solid at 0 K

model of a solid at a temperature above 0 K

- At **0 K** (–273°) the particles are **stationary**.
- At temperatures above 0 K the particles vibrate but cannot move from their positions.
- As the **temperature increases** the **vibrations** become **more energetic**.

LIQUIDS

Liquids take the shape of the container into which they are put.

liquids can flow

- Particles in a liquid are still fairly close together.
- The forces between particles are not as strong as in a solid and allow groups of particles to slide over each other. This is why liquids can flow.
- Particles in a liquid therefore do not have a fixed position.
- Liquids do not have a shape of their own. They take the shape of the container into which they are put.
- These groups of particles move around slowly.

a dye added to beaker of water

This mixing is called diffusion

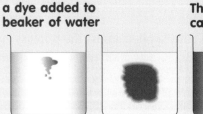

Because the liquid particles move around slowly the dye gradually mixes with the water.

GASES

- The _distances_ between particles in a gas are relatively _large_.
- Therefore they are almost _completely free of forces_ and so spread out and _fill any container_ into which they are placed.
- They are moving around at high speeds (approx. 500 m/s at room temperature).
- Gases diffuse (spread out and mix) more quickly than liquids.
- The directions in which they move have no pattern: they are _random motions_ (speed and direction).
- The gas particles inside this container are _continually bouncing off the sides_. It is these collisions with the sides of the container that _create the pressure_ inside the container.

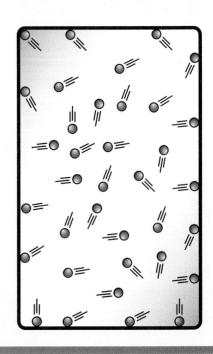

WHAT AFFECTS THE PRESSURE IN A GAS?

There are several factors that will affect the size of the pressure in a gas.

MASS

If <u>more</u> <u>gas</u> <u>particles</u> are pushed into the container there will be <u>more</u> <u>frequent</u> <u>collisions</u> and so the <u>pressure</u> <u>will</u> <u>increase</u>.

small mass of gas

larger mass of gas

few collisions per second, therefore low pressure

more collisions per second, therefore higher pressure

VOLUME

If the <u>volume</u> of the container is <u>decreased</u>, the particles will have less distance to travel between collisions. There will therefore be <u>more</u> <u>collisions</u> <u>per</u> <u>second</u>, i.e. the <u>pressure</u> <u>will</u> <u>increase</u>.

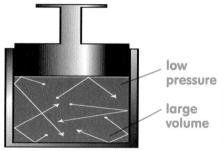

low pressure

large volume

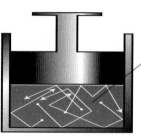

smaller volume and more collisions per second, therefore higher pressure

TEMPERATURE

If the <u>temperature</u> of a gas is <u>increased</u> its particles will <u>move</u> <u>faster</u>, there will be <u>more</u> <u>collisions</u> each second and there will again be an <u>increase</u> <u>in</u> <u>pressure</u>.

low temperature

few collisions per second, therefore low pressure

higher temperature

more collisions per second, therefore higher pressure

QUICK TEST

1. In which of the three states of matter:

   a) are the forces between particles strongest?   b) do particles fill the whole container in which they are placed?   c) are particles able to move even though there are strong forces between them?   d) do particles have fixed positions?

2. How is pressure created in a gas?

3. What is the effect on the pressure of a sample of gas in a container of doing each of the following:

   a) pushing more gas particles into the container?   b) lowering the temperature of the gas?
   c) compressing the gas by decreasing the volume of the container?

4. In which of the three states of matter can diffusion take place?

4. Liquids and gases.
3. a) Increases pressure.
   b) Decreases pressure.
   c) Increases pressure.
2. Particle collisions with the container wall.
1. a) solid, b) gas, c) liquid, d) solid.

ATOMIC STRUCTURE I

BACKGROUND

- For many years scientists thought that atoms were the smallest particles that could exist.
- With a greater understanding of electricity it was suggested that atoms must contain positive and negative charges.
- A scientist called J J Thomson suggested that atoms have a positive body which contains negative particles, like a pudding which contains plums.
- An experiment was carried out by two scientists called Johannes Wilhelm Geiger and Ernst Marsden. The results of this experiment suggested a different model for the atom, the nuclear atom.
- The experiment they carried out was called the alpha-particle scattering experiment.

How to make static electricity

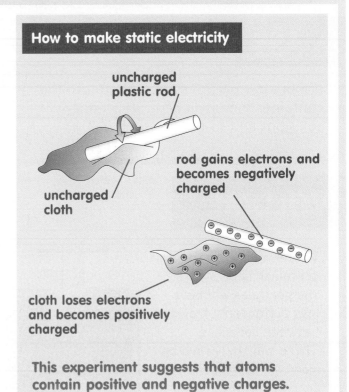

uncharged plastic rod

uncharged cloth

rod gains electrons and becomes negatively charged

cloth loses electrons and becomes positively charged

This experiment suggests that atoms contain positive and negative charges.

THE ALPHA-PARTICLE SCATTERING EXPERIMENT

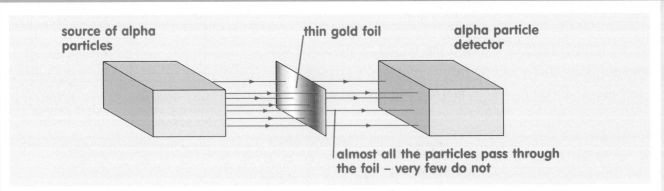

source of alpha particles

thin gold foil

alpha particle detector

almost all the particles pass through the foil – very few do not

- **Small particles called <u>alpha particles</u> were 'shot' at a <u>very</u> <u>thin</u> <u>piece</u> <u>of</u> <u>gold</u> <u>foil</u>.**
- **Most of the particles <u>passed</u> <u>straight</u> <u>through</u> <u>the</u> <u>foil</u> and were undeviated.**
- **This suggests that most of an atom is <u>empty</u> <u>space</u>.**
- **Some particles were deviated a little.**
- **A very small number <u>travelled</u> <u>back</u> almost in the direction from which they came.**
- **This suggests that most of the mass of an atom is concentrated in a <u>very</u> <u>small</u> <u>central</u> <u>nucleus</u> and that this centre must be positively charged.**
- **The model became known as the <u>nuclear</u> <u>atom</u>.**

THE NUCLEAR ATOM

STRUCTURE OF AN ATOM

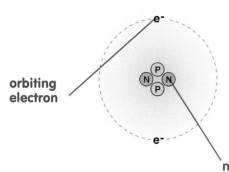

orbiting electron

e⁻

e⁻

nucleus – over 99.9% of the mass of the atom is here

- An atom has a <u>central core</u> called <u>the nucleus</u> which contains nearly <u>all the mass</u> of the atom.

- Within the nucleus are two types of particles: <u>protons</u> and <u>neutrons</u>.

- Protons have a <u>relative atomic mass of 1</u> and carry a charge of <u>+1</u>.

- Neutrons have a <u>relative atomic mass of 1</u> but carry <u>no charge</u>.

- <u>Orbiting the nucleus</u> at very high speeds are extremely small particles called electrons.

- Electrons have a <u>very small mass</u> (about one two-thousandth of a proton) and carry a charge of <u>−1</u>.

Summary Table

Particle	Place	Relative atomic mass	Relative charge
Proton	In nucleus	1	+1
Neutron	In nucleus	1	0
Electron	In orbit around nucleus	0 $\left(\frac{1}{2000}\right)$	-1

Key Terms

Make sure you understand these terms before moving on:

- Nuclear atom
- Nucleus
- Proton
- Neutron
- Electron

QUICK TEST

1. What was the name of the model of the atom suggested by Geiger and Marsden's experiment?
2. Why were only of few of the alpha particles deflected back in the direction from which they came?
3. Where are the neutrons in an atom?
4. What relative charge is carried by an electron?
5. Where are the electrons in an atom?

5. Orbiting the nucleus.
4. -1.
3. In the nucleus.
2. Because the nucleus of an atom is very small.
1. The nuclear atom.

ATOMIC STRUCTURE II

IMPORTANT FACTS ABOUT ATOMS

- Atoms have <u>no</u> <u>overall</u> <u>charge</u>. They are <u>neutral</u>.

- They must therefore <u>contain</u> <u>equal</u> <u>numbers</u> <u>of</u> <u>protons</u> <u>and</u> <u>electrons</u>.

- The number of protons an atom has in its nucleus is called the <u>proton</u> <u>number</u>, or the <u>atomic</u> <u>number</u>.

- The number of protons + the number of neutrons an atom has in its nucleus is called the <u>nucleon</u> <u>number</u>, or the <u>atomic</u> <u>mass</u>.

THE PERIODIC TABLE

There are over 100 different <u>elements</u>. Information about their <u>atomic structure</u> is contained in the <u>Periodic Table</u>.

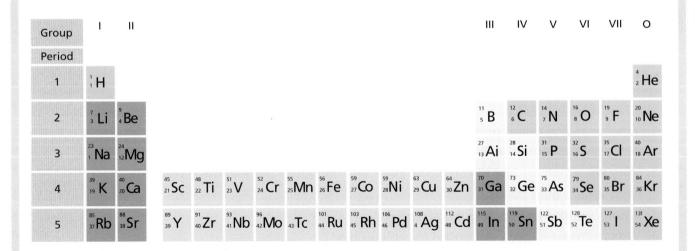

We can use this information to draw the atomic structure of an element.

DRAWING THE STRUCTURES OF ATOMS FROM THE PERIODIC TABLE

HELIUM

- Helium has a proton number of 2. Its nucleus contains two protons.

- Helium has a nucleon number of 4. Its nucleus contains two protons and two (4-2) neutrons.

- A helium atom is neutral, it must therefore have two orbiting electrons.

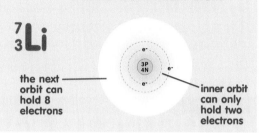

nucleon number → $^4_2$He ← symbol for element

proton number →

structure of helium atom

LITHIUM

- Lithium has a proton number of 3. Its nucleus contains three protons.

- Lithium has a nucleon number of 7. Its nucleus contains three protons and four (7-3) neutrons.

- A lithium atom is neutral, it must therefore have three orbiting electrons.

structure of lithium atom

$^7_3$Li

the next orbit can hold 8 electrons

inner orbit can only hold two electrons

POTASSIUM

- Potassium has a proton number of 19. Its nucleus contains 19 protons.

- Potassium has a nucleon number of 39. Its nucleus contains 20 (39-19) neutrons.

- A potassium atom is neutral, it must therefore have 19 orbiting electrons.

structure of potassium atom

$^{39}_{19}$K

this third orbit also holds eight electrons

ISOTOPES

this isotope is called chlorine –37

this isotope is called chlorine –35

Isotopes of chlorine

- Some atoms of the same element have <u>nuclei</u> with <u>different</u> <u>numbers</u> of <u>neutrons</u>.
- For example all atoms of chlorine have 17 protons in their nuclei but some atoms have 18 neutrons in their nuclei whilst others have 20.
- These different forms of the same element are called <u>isotopes</u>.

QUICK TEST

1. Using the periodic table, find out the proton number of oxygen and the nucleon number of nitrogen.

2. Draw the atomic structure of: a) $^9_4$Be
   b) $^{24}_{12}$Mg

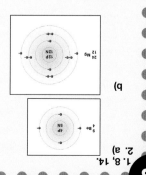

1. 8, 14.
2. a)

RADIOACTIVITY

ALPHA RADIATION (α)

- Alpha particles are **slow-moving helium nuclei**, i.e. they consist of **two protons and two neutrons.**
- They are **big and heavy** and so have **poor penetration** (just a few centimetres in air).
- They collide with lots of atoms, **knocking some of their electrons off** and **creating ions**.
- They are **very good ionisers**.
- An **ion** is an atom which has become charged by either losing or gaining electrons.
- They are **positively charged** and so can be **deflected by electric and magnetic fields**.

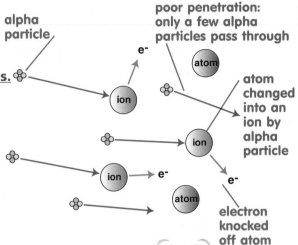

alpha particle

poor penetration: only a few alpha particles pass through

atom changed into an ion by alpha particle

electron knocked off atom

EXPOSURE TO RADIATION

- <u>Absorption</u> of any of the three types of radiation by living cells is potentially dangerous.
- Absorption may cause <u>cell damage</u> and lead to illnesses such as <u>cancer</u>.
- Higher levels of exposure to these radiations may <u>kill living cells</u>.
- Those at most risk, e.g. radiographers, wear <u>radiation badges</u>. These contain photographic film which, when developed, shows the <u>degree of exposure</u> to radiation for that worker.

EXPOSURE FROM SOURCES OUTSIDE THE BODY
- Alpha radiation is the least dangerous as it is the least penetrating and unlikely to reach any living cells.
- Beta and gamma are more dangerous because they are more penetrating.

EXPOSURE FROM SOURCES INSIDE THE BODY
- Alpha is the most dangerous radiation as it is most strongly absorbed by living cells and therefore causes most damage.
- Beta and gamma are not so dangerous as they are less likely to be absorbed by living cells.

Film badge dosimeter for monitoring exposure to radiation.

752145

SOURCES OF RADIOACTIVITY

- There are radioactive substances all around us.
- Some of them are man-made and used in hospitals, nuclear power stations and even in the home.
- Most of the radioactive substances around us are naturally occurring. They are in the ground, in the food we eat, and even in the air we breathe.
- Some radiation reaches us from space.
- The radiation produced by these sources is called <u>background radiation</u>.

SOURCES OF BACKGROUND RADIATION

medical sources

naturally occurring uranium isotopes found in granite

51%

14%

the air we breathe and the food we eat

12%

12%

10%

1%

gamma rays from rocks and soil

from space

less than 1% from leaks and fall out

- **Some substances give out <u>radiation</u> all the time. These substances are said to be <u>radioactive</u>.**
- **There are three types of radiation a substance might emit: alpha radiation, beta radiation and gamma rays.**

BETA RADIATION (β)

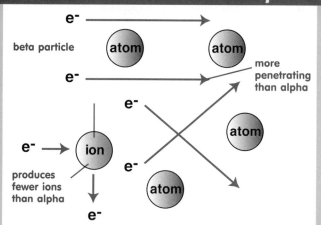

- These are <u>fast moving electrons</u>.
- They are small and therefore have <u>quite good penetrating powers</u> (up to about a metre in air).
- They do collide with atoms and produce ions, but not as many as the alpha particles.
- They are <u>negatively charged</u> and so can be <u>deflected by electric and magnetic fields</u>.

GAMMA RAYS (γ)

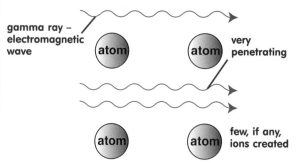

- These are <u>short-wavelength</u> electromagnetic <u>waves</u>, similar to X-rays.
- They <u>travel at the speed of light</u> and are <u>very penetrating</u> (they can travel almost unlimited distances through air).
- They do not hit many atoms as they travel through a material and so are <u>very poor ionisers</u>.
- Gamma radiation <u>carries no charge</u> and so is <u>unaffected by magnetic and electric fields</u>.

COMPARISON OF THE PROPERTIES OF ALPHA, BETA AND GAMMA RADIATION

Radiation	α	β	γ
Relative mass	4	Negligible (1/2000)	0
Relative charge	+2	–1	0
Relative ionising power	100000	1000	1
Approximate penetrating power in air	1–5 cm	10–80 cm	Almost unlimited

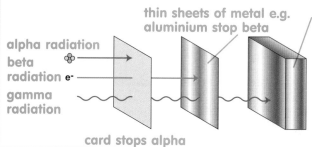

thin sheets of metal e.g. aluminium stop beta

thick sheets of dense metal or several metres of concrete needed to stop gamma

alpha radiation
beta radiation
gamma radiation

card stops alpha

undeviated gamma

light beta particles deviate a lot

heavy alpha particles deviate a little

source of radiation

Deflection of alpha, beta and gamma radiation in an electric field.

QUICK TEST

1. **Which type of radiation:**

   a) **is most penetrating?**   b) **is the best ioniser?**   c) **is negatively charged?**

   d) **is a fast moving electron?**   e) **is an electromagnetic wave?**

1. a) Gamma.
b) Alpha.
c) Beta.
d) Beta.
e) Gamma.

USES OF RADIOACTIVITY

QUALITY CONTROL

- Sheet material such as paper needs to be produced with a constant thickness.
- This can be monitored using the emissions from a radioactive source.
- A beta-emitting source, such as strontium-90, is placed above the paper.
- A beta detector is placed directly beneath it.
- If the paper becomes thinner more radiation reaches the detector and the pressure between the rollers is decreased.
- If the paper becomes thicker less radiation is detected and the pressure on the rollers is increased.
- Continuous monitoring like this guarantees that the thickness/quality of the paper is correct.
- This arrangement can also be used to monitor the quality of sheet metal but a gamma-emitting source replaces the stontium-90.

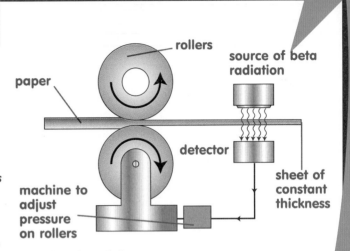

CARBON DATING

There are two isotopes of carbon.
- **Carbon-12**, which is **not radioactive**, and **carbon-14**, which is **radioactive**.
- Whilst a plant or animal is alive the ratio of these two isotopes within it remains the same.
- When the organism dies this ratio changes. By measuring this ratio scientists can determine how long ago the plant or animal died.

- **For example,** carbon-14 has a half-life of 5500 years, so if the ratio of carbon-14 to carbon-12 is half the value found in living organisms, that plant or animal has been dead for 5500 years.
- Uranium isotopes decay to form isotopes of lead. By measuring the ratio of uranium and lead isotopes in a sample of rock, its age can be found.

This shroud was thought to have been wrapped around the body of Jesus Christ until carbon-dating showed it to be just under 1000 years old.

RADIOACTIVE TRACERS

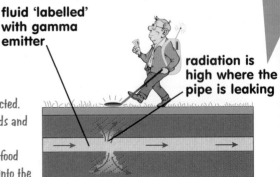

fluid 'labelled' with gamma emitter

radiation is high where the pipe is leaking

Radioisotopes can be used to monitor the flow of liquids and gases in pipes.
- A gamma-emitting radioisotope is added to the fluid flowing through the pipe.
- This material is called a tracer.
- If there is a leak in the pipe a higher concentration of gamma radiation will be detected.
- Using a radioisotope in this manner avoids the need to dig up whole sections of roads and piping in order to find the leak.
- Tracers can also be used to check the progress of fluids such as blood and digested food through the body. For example, sodium-24 is a radioisotope that can be introduced into the body to check for internal bleeding.

RADIOTHERAPY

Some forms of cancer can be removed by surgery. Others like brain tumours, because of their position, may require a different solution, e.g. radiotherapy.
- A narrow beam of radiation is directed at the tumour from different positions.
- A high dose of radiation needed to kill the cancerous cells only occurs within the tumour.
- In other places the dose is not large enough to cause cell damage.

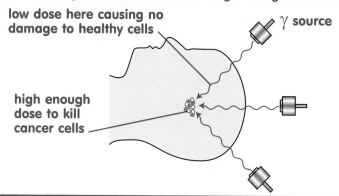

low dose here causing no damage to healthy cells

γ source

high enough dose to kill cancer cells

STERILISATION

- Food rots because of the presence and growth of bacteria.
- Cooling and freezing slows down the growth of the bacteria but does not prevent it.
- If food is exposed to gamma radiation before being frozen the bacteria are killed and the food keeps for much longer.
- This process is called <u>sterilisation</u>.
- Surgical instruments used to be sterilised by putting them in boiling water; nowadays these instruments are sterilised by exposing them to gamma radiation.

gamma source

unsterilised fruit

sterilised, germ-free fruit will last longer

conveyor belt

QUICK TEST

1. What kind of radiation should a source emit if it is to be used for monitoring the thickness of:

   a) card?

   b) sheets of steel?

2. What is the name given to a radioisotope which is injected into a fluid so that its flow can be monitored?

3. Why should a source which emits alpha radiation not be used to check the flow of blood through a body?

4. The treatment of cancer with radiation is called ………

5. Which type of radiation is used to sterilise surgical instruments?

6. Which radioactive isotope of carbon is used to date objects that were once alive?

1. a) Beta.
   b) Gamma.
2. Tracer.
3. It causes cell damage.
4. Radiotherapy.
5. Gamma.
6. Carbon-14.

THE EARTH AND BEYOND I

We live on a <u>planet</u> called the <u>Earth</u>. Although we cannot feel it, the <u>Earth</u> is <u>spinning</u>. The Earth <u>completes</u> <u>one</u> turn <u>every</u> <u>24</u> hours (one day).

This part of the Earth is receiving sunlight – it is daytime here.

This part of the Earth is not receiving sunlight – it is night-time here.

THE SEASONS

THE HIGHS AND LOWS OF THE SUN

- Because the Earth is turning, <u>the Sun appears to travel</u> across the sky <u>from the East to the West</u>.
- In the <u>summer</u> the Sun's path is <u>high in the sky</u>.
- In the <u>winter</u> its path is <u>much lower</u>.

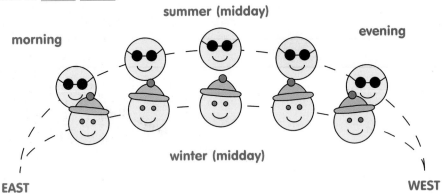

THE SEASONAL TILT

- <u>The Earth orbits</u> the Sun <u>once every year</u>.
- Because the Earth is <u>tilted</u> we experience <u>different seasons</u> – spring, summer, autumn and winter.
- When the northern part of the Earth is <u>tilted</u> <u>towards</u> the Sun it is <u>summer</u> in the northern hemisphere and <u>winter</u> in the southern hemisphere.
- When the northern part of the Earth is <u>tilted</u> <u>away</u> from the Sun it is <u>winter</u> in the northern hemisphere and <u>summer</u> in the southern hemisphere.

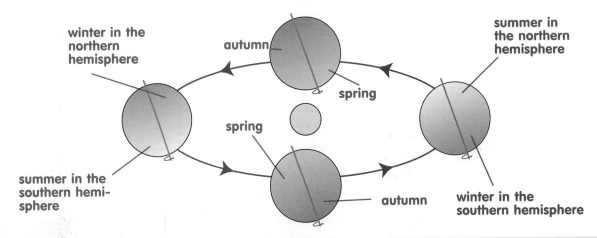

THE SOLAR SYSTEM

Our Solar System consists of a <u>star</u>, <u>a number of planets</u>, <u>moons</u>, <u>asteroids</u> and <u>comets</u>. We call <u>our star</u> <u>the Sun</u>. It contains over 99% of all the mass in our Solar System. The planets, their moons, the asteroids and the comets all orbit the Sun.

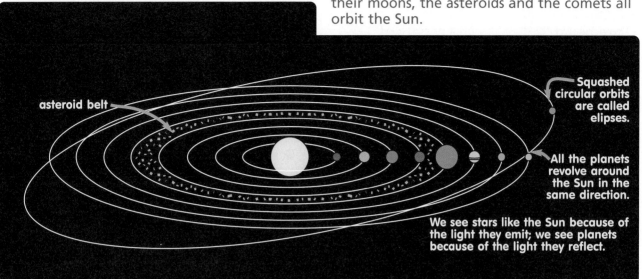

asteroid belt

Squashed circular orbits are called elipses.

All the planets revolve around the Sun in the same direction.

We see stars like the Sun because of the light they emit; we see planets because of the light they reflect.

- The Earth is one of <u>nine</u> planets. In order from the planet nearest the Sun they are: Mercury, Venus, Earth, Mars, Jupiter, Saturn, Uranus, Neptune and Pluto.
- We can remember the order using the sentence: <u>M</u>any <u>V</u>ery <u>E</u>nergetic <u>M</u>en <u>J</u>og <u>S</u>lowly <u>U</u>pto <u>N</u>ewport <u>P</u>agnell.
- We see stars like the Sun because of the light they <u>emit</u>. Stars are <u>luminous</u> objects.
- We see <u>planets</u> <u>and</u> <u>moons</u> because of the light they <u>reflect</u>. They are <u>non-luminous</u> objects.

INTERESTING (BUT NOT TO BE MEMORISED)

Quite often in an examination you will be given a table of facts about the Solar System and then asked questions about it:

Planet	Distance from the Sun (millions of km)	Orbit time in Earth years	Mass compared with the Earth	Surface temperature in °C
Mercury	60	0.2	0.05	350
Venus	110	0.6	0.8	
Earth	150	1.0	1.0	22
Mars	230	1.9	0.1	−30
Jupiter	775	11.9	318	−150
Saturn	1450	29.5	95	
Uranus	2900	84	15	−210
Neptune	4500	165	17	
Pluto	5900	248	0.1	−230

Try these:

1. Name one planet that is closer to the Sun than the Earth.

2. Name two planets further away from the Sun than Jupiter.

3. Which is the largest planet in our Solar System?

4. Estimate the surface temperatures of Venus and Saturn.

QUICK TEST

1. How long does it take for the Earth to complete one rotation about its axis?

2. How long does it take the Earth to make one complete orbit of the Sun?

3. What season is it in the southern hemisphere when the northern hemisphere is tilted towards the Sun?

4. Name one body in the sky which is a) luminous and b) non-luminous.

5. What shape are the orbits of the planets?

6. Where is the asteroid belt?

1. 1 day. 2. 1 year. 3. Winter. 4. a) The Sun, b) All planets and moons. 5. Elipses
6. Between the orbits of Mars and Jupiter.

GRAVITATIONAL FORCES

THE PLANETS

- The planets move in orbits because they are being 'pulled' by the gravity of the Sun.

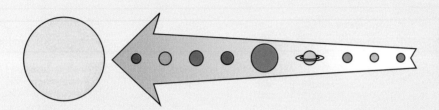

the gravitational pull of the Sun keeps the planets in their orbits

- Objects which are close to the Sun feel a stronger pull and follow very curved paths.
- Objects that are a long way from the Sun feel a weak pull and follow the less curved orbits.

ASTEROIDS

- Asteroids are lumps of rock orbiting the Sun.
- They vary in size from several metres to about 1000 km.
- Most asteroids are found in a belt between Mars and Jupiter.

COMETS

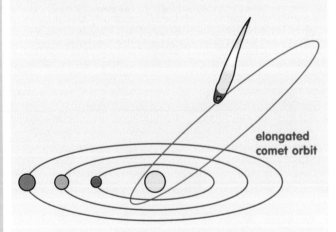

elongated comet orbit

- Comets are large, rock-like pieces of ice that orbit the Sun.
- They have very elliptical orbits.
- They travel fastest when they are close to the Sun because the gravitational forces here are large.
- Close to the Sun some of a comet's ice melts, creating a long tail.

SATELLITES

- **Moons** are large natural satellites that orbit a planet.
- We have just one moon but some planets have several e.g. Mars has two, Jupiter has 16 and Saturn has 21.

Artificial satellites launched by man can be put into orbit around the Earth. They have three main uses:

- To look away from the Earth into deep space, e.g. the Hubble telescope.
- To monitor conditions on the surface of the Earth, e.g. weather satellites. Satellites that monitor the whole of the Earth's surface are often put into low polar orbits.
- Geostationary satellites that stay above the same place on the Earth's surface the whole time, e.g. communications satellites.

THE EARTH AND BEYOND II

STARS

- Our Sun is a <u>star</u>.
- It is just one of millions of stars that make up the <u>galaxy</u> we live in.
- Our galaxy is called the <u>Milky</u> <u>Way</u>.

- In the <u>Universe</u> there are billions of galaxies. They are separated by distances that are often millions of times greater than the distances between stars within a galaxy.

side view

we are about here

← 20,000 light years →

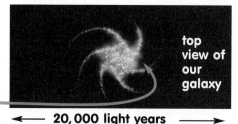

top view of our galaxy

The Milky Way is a spiral galaxy.

← 20,000 light years →

HOW STARS ARE BORN

- Stars form when <u>clouds</u> <u>of</u> <u>gases</u> are pulled together by <u>gravitational</u> <u>forces</u>.
- These forces cause the gases to be <u>compressed</u>. As a result there is a <u>very</u> <u>large</u> <u>increase</u> <u>in</u> <u>temperature</u>.
- This temperature increase sets off <u>nuclear</u> <u>reactions</u> which <u>fuse</u> <u>hydrogen</u> <u>nuclei</u> <u>together</u>.
- These reactions release large amounts of energy as heat and light. A star is born.
- <u>Smaller</u> <u>concentrations</u> <u>of</u> <u>dust</u> and <u>gases</u> may form some distance away from the developing star. These may eventually <u>become</u> <u>planets</u> <u>and</u> <u>their</u> <u>moons</u>.

QUICK TEST

1. What forces keep all the planets in orbit around the Sun?

2. Where during their orbit of the Sun do comets travel fastest?

3. What is a natural satellite?

4. Give three uses for artificial satellites.

5. What is the name of our nearest star?

6. What is the name of the galaxy in which we live?

7. What forces bring together the particles of gas to form a star?

8. What kinds of reactions cause the temperature of a forming star to increase?

1. Gravitational forces.   2. When they are closest to the Sun.   3. A moon.
4. Looking into space, weather forecasting and communications.
5. The Sun.   6. The Milky Way.   7. Gravitational forces.
8. Nuclear fusion reactions.

EXAM QUESTIONS – Use the questions to test your progress. Check your answers on page 95.

1. Name the three particles that are found inside an atom. Which two of these particles carry a charge?
....

2. Name five different types of bodies that make up our Solar System.
....

3. How is the apparent path taken by the Sun across the sky in winter different to its path in summer?
....

4. What forces hold the planets in orbits?
....

5. The diagram below shows the penetrating powers of three different types of radioactivity. Identify the type of radiation emitted by each of the sources.

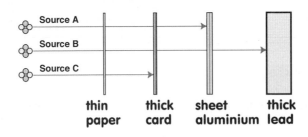

....

6. Which of the three different types of radioactive emission:
   a) is not affected by a magnetic field?
....

   b) carries a negative charge?
....

   c) creates lots of ions as it travels through matter?
....

   d) travels at the speed of light in a vacuum?
....

7. What is a satellite? Give one example of a) a natural satellite and b) an artificial satellite.
....

8. Which of the three states of matter:
   a) has the strongest forces between its particles?..
   b) has almost no forces between its particles?...
   c) is able to flow?...
   d) has its own shape?..

9. What is an asteroid?
....

10. Who is likely to wear a radiation badge or dosimeter and what does it do?
....

11. From what materials are stars formed?
....

12. Name three medical uses for radioisotopes.
....

13. Name two industrial uses for radioisotopes.

....

....

14. Which experiment lead to the nuclear model of the atom?

....

15. What are isotopes? Give an example of a pair of isotopes.

....

16. How many electrons do the following atoms have in their orbits:
    a) $^{7}_{3}Li$ b) $^{24}_{12}Ca$ c) $^{16}_{8}O$?

....

17. Name:
    a) two natural sources of radioactivity

....

    b) two artificial or manmade sources of radioactivity.

....

18. Why is a source of alpha radiation outside the body unlikely to cause damage to vital organs inside the body?

....

....

19. a) What is a radioactive tracer?

....

    b) Give one example of how a radioactive tracer is used?

....

20. Explain how the particles of a gas in a container create pressure. Explain why the pressure of the gas is likely to increase if its temperature is raised.

....

....

How did you do?

1–5	correct ....start again
6–10	correct ....getting there
11–15	correct ....good work
16–20	correct ....excellent

Forces and Motion

1. 10 m/s.
2. 270 km.
3. 25 s.
4. With tiredness the stopping distance will increase.
5. Pressure in a liquid increases with depth and submarines have to dive deep below the surface.
6. 50 J.
7. Slow down, speed up and change direction.
8. It is streamlined so there is less water resistance.
9. a) He is travelling at a constant speed.
    b) He is stationary.
    c) He is travelling at a lower constant speed.
10. Hydraulic jack, car brakes.
11. Oil, water, grease, etc.
12. Air resistance will equal weight; the diver will fall at his terminal velocity.
13. 24 Nm or 2400 Ncm.
14. 20 N.
15. 0.5 m².
16. 5m/s².
17. a) X = reaction, Y = weight, Z = friction
    b) All the forces acting on the object are balanced
    c) 30 N
    d) Add a lubricant, e.g. oil or water; put the object on wheels
18. a) 50 m   b) 800 N   c) 40 000 J   d) 1600 W
19. a) 10 N   b) 3.5 cm   c) elastic   d) permanently stretched

Energy

1. a) Electric motor   b) Generator or dynamo
    c) Solar cell
2. a) Sound   b) Chemical.
3. Elastic potential energy.
4. Gravitational potential energy.
5. a) Radiation   b) Convection   c) Conduction.
6. a) An energy source which will not be exhausted
    b) Wind energy, tidal energy, solar energy
7. a) Coal, oil and gas   b) Once they have been used they can not be replaced   c) Wood
8. Use renewable sources of energy; insulate homes and factories to reduce energy wastage; develop more efficient machines and generators.
9. Loft insulation, cavity wall insulation, double glazing, underlay and carpets, draft excluders and curtains.
10. a) It is the trapped layer of air between the glass that reduces heat-loss, not the glass itself.
    b) Radiation.
11. a) Room temperature   b) Its temperature increases more   c) To help keep houses cool by reflecting radiation.
12. 1-B, 2-D, 3-A, 4-C
13. a) Dark-coloured surfaces are good absorbers of radiation   b) To reduce heat loss   c) To reduce heat loss but still allow radiation to reach the pipes and collector plate.
14. 60%
15. 40 J
16. a) A = one year   B = four years   C = 60 years
    b) The hot-water jacket
17. a) Gravitational potential energy   b) Kinetic energy   c) Water is stored in the top lake until electrical energy is needed   d) 75%

Waves

1. Energy.
2. A = amplitude, B = wavelength.
3. Reflection, refraction and diffraction.
4. B.
5. Light travels much faster than sound.
6. Low.
7. Vacuum.
8. 25 Hz.
9. i) A   ii) C   iii) B   iv) D
10. The reflection of a sound wave   b) 750 m
    c) An echo would be heard sooner.
11. Violet; Spectrum.
12. SOund, Navigation, And Ranging.
13. A specially shaped piece of glass or plastic used to bend light.
14. It slows down and bends towards the normal; it slows down but does not change direction.
15. 3 m behind the mirror.
16. Sounds with frequencies that are so high they can not be heard by human beings; prenatal scanning.
17. a) The critical angle   b) i) the ray is refracted and partially reflected   ii) the ray is totally internally reflected.
18. a) Total internal reflection   b) 90°   c) Periscope

19. It always strikes the inner surface at an angle greater than the critical angle and so is always totally internally reflected; an endoscope or cable television.

20. Ear defenders are worn over the ears to prevent damage to hearing. Workers using noisy machinery should wear them.

21. a) A = ɣ (gamma) rays, B = radio waves.
    b) They can all be reflected, refracted and undergo diffraction.
    They all travel at the same speed in a vacuum.
    c) ɣ (gamma) rays have higher frequency and shorter wavelength.
    d) Microwaves and infra-red waves.
    e) Microwaves, radio waves and visible light.
    f) Ultra-violet waves, X-rays and gamma rays.
    g) X-rays.

Electricity and Electromagnetism

1. They repel.
2. They attract.
3. Protons, neutrons and electrons; electrons.
4. It is a non-magnetic material.
5. Electrostatic paint spraying, removing dust particles from fumes.
6. Iron is magnetically soft and is used in electromagnets; steel is magnetically hard and is used to make permanent magnets.
7. The magnet's north pole will point northwards.
8. They can be turned on and off.
9. a) Circuit A is complete, Circuit B is incomplete.
    b) Place the material across the gap in the circuit. If the bulb now glows the material is a conductor, if it does not it is an insulator.
10. The outer casing.
11. Parallel circuit.
12. Diode.
13. A resistor whose resistance decreases in bright light; controlling street lights.
14. Larger current, more turns on coil, stronger magnetic field; the split ring changes the direction of the current in the coil every half turn.
15. More coils, turn faster, stronger magnet.
16. 3V.
17. 6 units, 66 p
18. Direct current is in only one direction; alternating current flows back and forth, i.e. it changes direction.

19. Less energy is lost in the wires and cables this way.
20. 1200 W.
21. 24 Ω.
22. 240 V.
23. 5 A.
24. a) 20 V   b) step-up transformer.

Atoms and Radioactivity and the Earth and Beyond

1. Protons, neutrons and electrons; Protons and electrons carry a charge.
2. Sun, planets, moons, asteroids and comets.
3. The path in winter is lower.
4. Gravitational forces.
5. a) Beta b) Gamma c) Alpha
6. a) Gamma b) Beta c) Alpha d) Gamma
7. An object that orbits a planet; a) The Moon b) A weather satellite.
8. a) solid b) gas c) liquid and gas d) solid.
9. A lump of rock orbiting the Sun.
10. Someone who works with radioactive materials; a dosimeter measures the amount of radiation to which the worker has been exposed.
11. Dust and gas.
12. Radiotherapy, sterilisation of surgical instruments and radioactive tracers (bloodstream).
13. Quality control, food preservation, radioactive tracers (pipes).
14. The alpha-particle scattering experiment.
15. Isotopes are nuclei of the same element that have different numbers of neutrons, e.g. Chlorine-35 and Chlorine-37.
16. a) 3 b) 12 c) 8.
17. a) In the ground (rocks), in the air b) Equipment in hospitals, nuclear power stations.
18. Alpha radiation cannot penetrate skin.
19. a) Radioactive material used to monitor flow or movement b) Add to bloodstream to check for internal bleeding and blockages.
20. By colliding with the sides of the container. Particles will move faster, have more collisions each second and therefore there will be an increase in pressure.

INDEX

INDEX

96